Impact maths 2 G

1 Understanding number   1

2 Symmetry and angles   26

3 Multiplication and division   41

4 Working with algebra   63

5 Number patterns   73

6 Fractions   86

7 Probability   100

8 Decimals and percentages   112

9 Shape and measure   132

About this book

Impact maths provides a complete course to help you achieve your best in your Key Stage 3 Mathematics course. This book will help you understand and remember mathematical ideas, solve mathematical problems with and without the help of a calculator and develop your mental maths skills.

Exercises you should try without the help of a calculator are marked with this symbol:

Finding your way around

To help you find your way around when you are studying use the:

- **edge marks** shown on the front pages – these help you get to the right unit quickly

- **contents list** and **index** – these list all the key ideas covered in the book and help you turn straight to them.

- **links** in the margin – these show when an idea elsewhere in the book may be useful:

There is more about division on page 43.

Remembering key ideas

We have provided clear explanations of the key ideas you need throughout the book with **worked examples** showing you how to answer questions. **Key points** you need to remember look like this:

■ **The distance around the edge of a shape is its perimeter.**

and are listed in a **summary** at the end of each unit.

Investigations and information technology

Two units focus on particular skills you need for your course:

- **using and applying mathematics** (unit 16) – shows you some ways of investigating mathematical problems.

- **calculators and computers** (unit 17) – shows you some ways of using calculators and computers and will help with mental maths practice.

10 Positive and negative numbers   147

11 Graphs   168

12 Handling data   182

13 Formulae and equations   201

14 Perimeter, area and volume   215

15 Averages   232

16 Using and applying mathematics   247

17 Calculators and computers   254

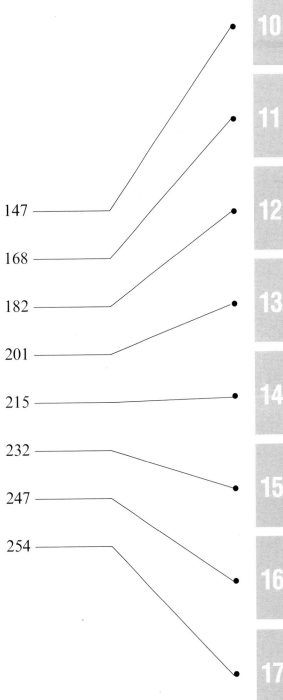

Heinemann Educational Publishers
Halley Court, Jordan Hill, Oxford, OX2 8EJ
a division of Reed Educational & Professional Publishing Ltd
Heinemann is a registered trademark of Reed Educational & Professional Publishing Ltd

OXFORD   MELBOURNE   AUCKLAND
JOHANNESBURG   BLANTYRE   GABORONE
IBADAN   PORTSMOUTH NH (USA)   CHICAGO

First published 2000

ISBN 0 435 01794 2

02 01
10 9 8 7 6 5 4 3

Designed and typeset by Tech-Set Ltd, Gateshead, Tyne and Wear
Illustrated by Barry Atkinson, Barking Dog and Tech-Set
Cover design by Miller, Craig and Cocking
Printed and bound by Edelvives, Spain

Acknowledgements
The authors and publishers would like to thank the following for permission to use photographs:
P63, P73, P147: Science Photo Library. P137: Telegraph Colour Library. P191: J.Allan Cash.
P193, P199, P242: Empics. P100: Moviestore. P100, P101: FLPA. P107: BBC.

Cover Photo by Tony Stone Images.

Publishing team

Editorial	Design	Author team	
Philip Ellaway	Phil Richards	David Benjamin	Gina Marquess
Nigel Green	Colette Jacquelin	Sue Bright	Christine Medlow
Shaheen Hassan	Mags Robertson	Tony Clough	Graham Newman
Sarah Caton		Gareth Cole	Sheila Nolan
Gwen Allingham	**Production**	Diana DeBrida	Keith Pledger
Harry Smith	David Lawrence	Ray Fraser	Ian Roper
	Joanne Morgan	Peter Jolly	Mike Smith
	Jason Wyatt	David Kent	John Sylvester

Tel:01865 888058   email:info.he@heinemann.co.uk

Contents

1   Understanding number

1.1	Place value	Two-digit and three-digit numbers	1–3
1.2	Numbers larger than a thousand	Extending place value	3–4
1.3	Ordering numbers	Putting numbers in order of size	5–7
1.4	Ordering numbers with the same first digit	Putting numbers in order of size	7–8
1.5	Mental maths	Number bonds to 20	8–11
1.6	Adding and subtracting multiples of 10	Working with 10's	11–12
1.7	Rounding to the nearest 10	Rounding whole numbers to the nearest 10	12–14
1.8	Adding and subtracting multiples of 100	Working with 100s	14
1.9	Rounding to the nearest 100	Rounding whole numbers to the nearest 100	15–16
1.10	Checking answers by estimation	Using rounding to check a calculator answer	16–17
1.11	Adding and subtracting a multiple of 10 to a 2-digit number	Adding and subtracting 10s	18–19
1.12	Mental maths with 2-digit numbers	Mental strategies with 2-digit numbers	19–21
1.13	Adding numbers on paper	Pencil and paper methods (adding)	22
1.14	Subtracting numbers on paper	Pencil and paper methods (subtracting)	23–24
	Summary of key points		24

2   Symmetry and angles

2.1	Symmetrical shapes	Lines and rotational symmetry	26–28
2.2	Measuring turns	Introducing degrees	29
2.3	Angle types	Acute, obtuse and right angles	30
2.4	Measuring angles	Using a protractor	31–32
2.5	Drawing angles	Constructing angles	32
2.6	Estimating angles	Estimating the size of an angle	33–34
2.7	Angles on lines	Angles that make a straight line add up to 180°	34–35
2.8	Angles at a point	Angles which add to 360° and Opposite angles are equal	35–37
2.9	Angles in shapes	Describing angles using letters	37–38
2.10	Angles in a triangle	Angle sums of a triangle	39–40
	Summary of key points		40

3 Multiplication and division

3.1	Multiplication up to 10×10	Table facts to 10×10	41–42
3.2	Dividing	Inverse table facts to 10×10	43–44
3.3	Remainders in division	Answers with remainders	44–45
3.4	Multiplication and division up to 10×10	Using table knowledge	45–47
3.5	Multiples	Odd and even numbers and multiples	47–49
3.6	Factors	A simple introduction to factors	49–51
3.7	Square numbers and square roots	What squares and square roots are	51–52
3.8	Multiplying 2- and 3-digit numbers by a 1-digit number	Using pencil and paper methods	52–55
3.9	Multiplying a 3-digit number by a 2-digit number	Using pencil and paper methods	56
3.10	Dividing a 3-digit number by a 1-digit number	Beginning long division	57–58
3.11	Dividing a 3-digit number by a 2-digit number	Long division	58–61
	Summary of key points		61

4 Working with algebra

4.1	Using letters to represent numbers	Letters in place of numbers	63–64
4.2	Collecting letters	Only 1 letter involved	65–66
4.3	Collecting like terms	Multiples of the same letter only	66–68
4.4	Simplifying expressions	Collecting like terms	68–69
4.5	Multiplying in algebra	$a \times b = ab$	69–70
4.6	Multiplying terms together	As in $4a \times 5b = 20ab$	70–72
	Summary of key points		72

5 Number patterns

5.1	Patterns from matchsticks and dots	Continuing patterns and finding the rules which generate them	73–75
5.2	Number machines	Finding the output after operations	76–80
5.3	Inverse operations	Undoing an operation	81–83
5.4	Number sequences and series	Generating sequences by rule	83–85
	Summary of key points		85

6 Fractions

6.1	Fractions all around	Recognizing fractions	86–87
6.2	Mixed numbers and improper fractions	Using both forms	88–90

6.3	Finding a fraction of a quantity	Working out the fractions of amounts in context	91–92
6.4	Finding more than one part	Numerators other than 1	92–93
6.5	Equivalent fractions	Finding fractions of equal value	93–96
6.6	Adding and subtracting fractions	Same denominator only	96–98
Summary of key points			98

7 Probability

7.1	The language of probability	Impossible, possible, certain	100–102
7.2	The likelihood scale	Probabilities in words	102–103
7.3	Using numbers to represent probabilities	The probability scale 0–1	103–104
7.4	Events and outcomes	More probability language	105–106
7.5	Calculating probabilities with one successful outcome	Probabilities which are $1/n$	107
7.6	Calculating probabilities with more than one successful outcome	Probabilities which are x/n	108–110
Summary of key points			110

8 Decimals and percentages

8.1	Decimal numbers	Extending place value to hundredths	112–113
8.2	Adding and subtracting decimals	Using pencil and paper methods	114–116
8.3	Multiplying and dividing decimals by 10, 100 and 1000	Making use of place value to multiply and divide	117–119
8.4	Multiplying decimals by whole numbers	Using long multiplication	120–121
8.5	Dividing decimals by whole numbers	Using long division	122–123
8.6	Writing decimal numbers in size order	Putting decimals in order of size	123–124
8.7	Understanding percentages	Showing 100% as the whole amount	125–126
8.8	Fractions, decimals and percentages	Converting between all three	126–129
8.9	Finding a percentage of an amount	Multiplying with the decimal equivalent	129–130
Summary of key points			130

9 Shape and measure

9.1	Points, lines and shapes	Using letters to identify shapes	132
9.2	Quadrilaterals	Square, rectangle, rhombus, kite, parallelogram and trapezium	133–134
9.3	Circles	Naming parts of the circle	135–136
9.4	Solid shapes	Cuboid, cube, pyramid, prism, sphere, cylinder, cone and hemisphere	137–138

9.5	Drawing solid shapes	How to sketch a solid	138–139
9.6	Nets	Nets of solids	140
9.7	Measure	Introducing millimetres	141
9.8	Capacity	Litres and millilitres	142–143
9.9	Imperial measure	Using well known equivalents	143–144
9.10	Time	Time between events	144–145

Summary of key points   146

10   Positive and negative numbers

10.1	Using temperatures	To show plus and minus	147–148
10.2	Writing temperatures in order of size	Using a thermometer	149–151
10.3	Moving between positive and negative temperatures	Temperature rise and fall	151–153
10.4	Using a vertical number line	Using a number line	153–155
10.5	Counting on or back	Going up or down, more or less	156–158
10.6	Working with positive and negative numbers	Beginning to add and subtract	158–160
10.7	Using a horizontal number line	Using a number line	160–163
10.8	Ordering positive and negative numbers	Further use of the number line	163–165
10.9	Continuing number patterns	Generating sequences by counting	165–167

Summary of key points   167

11   Graphs

11.1	Coordinates in the first quadrant	First quadrant only	168–169
11.2	Plotting coordinates	In the first quadrant	170–171
11.3	Lines on graphs	Naming vertical and horizontal lines	171–174
11.4	Coordinates in all 4 quadrants	Extending to all quadrants	174–175
11.5	Drawing coordinate grids	Axes and scales	176
11.6	Using conversion graphs	Temperature and imperial/metric	177–181

Summary of key points   181

12   Handling data

12.1	Collecting and organizing data	Using tally charts	182–184
12.2	Displaying data	Pictograms and bar charts	185–188
12.3	Dealing with larger numbers	Handling greater frequencies	188–191
12.4	Dual bar graphs	Dual bar graphs	191–193
12.5	Types of data	Discrete and continuous	193–195
12.6	Grouping data	Using equal class intervals	195–199

Summary of key points   200

13 Formulae and equations

13.1	Word formulae	Working out using word formulae	201–202
13.2	Using letters to represent numbers	Using letters	202–203
13.3	Using letters in formulae	Writing simple formulae	203–205
13.4	Formulae with two operations	Introducing 2-step formulae	205–207
13.5	Substituting into algebraic formulae		207–208
13.6	Solving equations	Solving equations by inspection	209–210
13.7	Solving equations using number machines	Solving equations by using inverse operations	210–212
13.8	Using algebra to solve equations	Using the balancing technique	212–214
Summary of key points			214

14 Perimeter, area and volume

14.1	Perimeter and area	Using counting methods	215–217
14.2	Perimeter and area of a rectangle	Using the word formulae	217–220
14.3	Area of a right-angled triangle	Using half base × height	220–222
14.4	Composite shapes	Working with shapes made from triangles and rectangles	222–223
14.5	Curved sided shapes	Area by counting squares	224–226
14.6	Volume	Counting cubes	227–228
14.7	Volume of a cuboid	Using a word formula	229–230
Summary of key points			230

15 Averages

15.1	The mode	Finding the mode from discrete lists	232–234
15.2	Using a table or chart to find the mode	Finding the mode in bar charts and frequency tables	234–237
15.3	The median	Finding the median from a list	238–240
15.4	The mean	Working out the mean for lists of discrete data	241–242
15.5	The range	Finding the range of lists of data	242–244
15.6	Comparing data	Comparing sets of data by their mean and range	244–245
Summary of key points			246

16 Using and applying mathematics

| **Investigation guidelines** | Investigating shaking hands, where everyone shakes hands with everyone else. | 247–253 |

17 Calculators and computers

17.1 **Using your square root key** Investigating the $\sqrt{x}$ key 254–255
17.2 **Generating sequences** Using a spreadsheet 255–256
17.3 **Percentage** $\times\ \%$ and divide by 100 257–258
17.4 **Number machines** Further spreadsheet methods 258–259
17.5 **Handling data** Spreadsheets working out mean, mode, median and range 259–262
17.6 **Angles and polygons** Using the WinLogo program 262–264
17.7 **Fractions** Making use of the fraction key 264–266

1 Understanding number

1.1 Place value

You can write any number
using the digits
0, 1, 2, 3, 4, 5, 6, 7, 8 and 9.

■ **The value of each digit depends
on its place in the number**

The digit 3 means:

Hundreds	Tens	Units	
3 hundreds = 300	③	8	2	Three hundred and eighty two
3 tens = 30	8	③	2	Eight hundred and thirty two
3 units = 3	2	8	③	Two hundred and eighty three

■ **382 is a three-digit number
38 is a two-digit number**

Example 1

What does the 5 mean in each of these numbers?
(a) 359   **(b)** 528   **(c)** 705   **(d)** 75

You write the answers like this:
(a) 5 tens = 50   **(b)** 5 hundreds = 500   **(c)** 5 units = 5   **(d)** 5 units = 5

Example 2

(a) Write six hundred and eighty two as a number.
(b) Write three hundred and seventeen as a number.
(c) Write six hundred and two as a number.

You write:
(a) 682   **(b)** 317   **(c)** 602 —————— You put 0 in the
tens place to show
there are no tens.

Exercise 1A

1 What does the 6 mean in each of these numbers?
    (a) 867   **(b)** 296   **(c)** 651
    (d) 601   **(e)** 610   **(f)** 61

Hint: It may help to draw a place value diagram.

6 tens = 60

2 What does the 9 mean in each of these numbers?
    (a) 952   **(b)** 497   **(c)** 905
    (d) 95   **(e)** 59   **(f)** 729

3 What does the 0 mean in each of these numbers?
    (a) 706   **(b)** 380   **(c)** 70
    (d) 203   **(e)** 0   **(f)** 760

4 Look at the numbers on these tickets.
Which number has:
    (a) 4 hundreds and 2 units?
    (b) 4 tens and 2 units?
    (c) 4 hundreds and 2 tens?
    (d) 8 hundreds and 1 unit?
    (e) 8 hundreds and 1 ten?
    (f) 8 tens and 3 units?

5 Write as a number:
    (a) Four hundred and seven.
    (b) Nine hundred and six.
    (c) Three hundred and nine.
    (d) Eight hundred and one.
    (e) Four hundred and eight.
    (f) Five hundred and two.

6 This table shows the locker numbers of six students.
Whose locker number is:
    (a) Four hundred and seventeen?
    (b) Nine hundred and fifteen?
    (c) Nine hundred and sixteen?
    (d) Three hundred and thirteen?
    (e) Three hundred and nineteen?
    (f) Four hundred and twelve?

Name	Locker number
Karim	319
Mandy	412
Tessa	417
Vijay	313
Janet	915
Alan	916

7 Write as a number:

(a) Four hundred and seventy.
(b) Nine hundred and sixty
(c) Three hundred and ninety.
(d) Seven hundred and fifty
(e) Six hundred and twenty.
(f) Three hundred and thirty.

8 These students each wrote down a 3-digit number. Who wrote down:

(a) Seven hundred and eighty three?
(b) Five hundred and thirty six?
(c) Nine hundred and sixty four?
(d) Seven hundred and fifty two?
(e) Five hundred and seventy seven?
(f) Nine hundred and forty nine?

1.2 Numbers larger than a thousand

■ **A place value diagram can help you read large numbers:**

The digit 7 means:

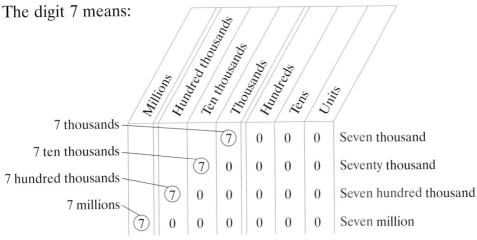

You read and write large numbers like this:

56 749 Fifty six thousand seven hundred and forty nine

834 276 Eight hundred and thirty four thousand two hundred and seventy six

a space like this shows you where the thousands end

Example 3

What does the 7 stand for in each of these numbers?

(a) 729 543   **(b)** 257 928   **(c)** 678 025   **(d)** 7 423 025

You write the answer like this:

(a) 7 hundred-thousands   **(b)** 7 thousands
or seven hundred thousand   or seven thousand
or 700 000   or 7 000

(c) 7 ten-thousands   **(d)** 7 millions
or seventy thousand   or seven million
or 70 000   or 7 000 000

Example 4

Write the number 2 437 208 in words.

Use a place value diagram.

You write two million four hundred and thirty seven thousand, two hundred and eight.

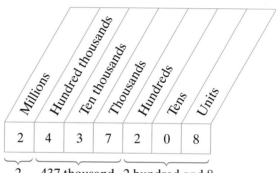

Exercise 1B

1 What does the 3 stand for in each of these numbers?
(a) 394 826 **(b)** 473 092 **(c)** 936 405 **(d)** 842 356

2 What does the 6 stand for in each of these numbers?
(a) 296 804 **(b)** 364 802 **(c)** 693 281 **(d)** 63 400
(e) 806 918 **(f)** 68 294 **(g)** 6 584 **(h)** 463 987

3 Write these numbers in words.
(a) 582 430 **(b)** 195 659 **(c)** 305 451 **(d)** 470 301

4 Write as numbers.
(a) Two hundred and twenty seven thousand, four hundred and thirty two.
(b) Six hundred and thirty four thousand, three hundred and two.
(c) Forty eight thousand, seven hundred and sixteen.
(d) Ninety six thousand and thirty eight.
(e) Six hundred and two thousand, three hundred and six.
(f) Four hundred and two thousand and fifty four.

1.3 Ordering numbers

Which of these TV sets is cheaper?

Look at the digit with the highest place value.
It will be the digit furthest to the left.

The digit with the highest place value in 436 is 4:

Its value is 4 hundreds = 400

The digit with the highest place value in 389 is 3:

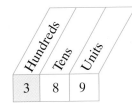

Its value is 3 hundreds = 300

3 hundreds is less than 4 hundreds so the TV which costs £389 is cheaper.

■ **The digit with the highest place value is on the left of the number**

The digit with the highest place value is also called the most significant digit.

Example 5

Which is bigger 294 or 314?

Think of a place value diagram:

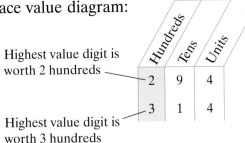

Highest value digit is worth 2 hundreds

Highest value digit is worth 3 hundreds

3 hundreds is greater than 2 hundreds so 314 is larger than 294.

Example 6

Which is smaller 85 or 453?

The digit with the highest place value in 85 is 8, it is worth 8 tens or 80.
The digit with the highest place value in 453 is 4, it is worth 4 hundreds or 400.
8 tens is less than 4 hundreds so 85 is less than 453.

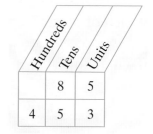

Hundreds	Tens	Units
	8	5
4	5	3

Exercise 1C

1 Which is bigger?
   (a) 38 or 29   (b) 53 or 45   (c) 86 or 95
   (d) 78 or 65   (e) 75 or 36   (f) 63 or 42

2 Which is bigger?
   (a) 186 or 223   (b) 297 or 326   (c) 452 or 398
   (d) 861 or 592   (e) 383 or 943   (f) 426 or 729

3 Which is smaller?
   (a) 86 or 132   (b) 237 or 79   (c) 342 or 87
   (d) 76 or 526   (e) 846 or 98   (f) 54 or 530

4 Put > or < in each box to make a true statement.

   (a) 35 ☐ 84   (b) 97 ☐ 62   (c) 35 ☐ 58

   (d) 643 ☐ 528   (e) 575 ☐ 291   (f) 416 ☐ 71

   (g) 236 ☐ 742   (h) 87 ☐ 349

Remember:
46 < 62 means 46 is less than 62
58 > 37 means 58 is greater than 37.

5 Decide whether each statement is true or false:
   (a) 86 > 35   (b) 46 > 51   (c) 36 < 54
   (d) 96 < 172   (e) 249 < 654   (f) 821 < 964
   (g) 721 > 634   (h) 416 < 89

6 Which city is closer to Paris: Marseille or Nice?

| Paris to Nice | 930 km |
| Paris to Marseille | 785 km |

7 Which holds more: a 500 ml bottle of drink or a 440 ml can of drink?

8 The table shows the points scored by each house in a school's house competition.

House	Red	Blue	Green	Yellow
Points	468	643	597	359

(a) Which house scored the most points?
(b) Which house scored the least points?

1.4 Ordering numbers with the same first digit

Which bike costs more?

The digit with the highest place value is the same so look at the next highest.

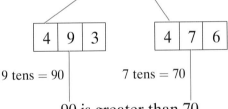

9 tens = 90   7 tens = 70

90 is greater than 70

So the bike for £493 costs more.

Example 7

(a) Which is greater 748 or 762?
7④8   7⑥2

40 is less than 60

So 762 is greater than 748.

(b) Which is smaller 362 or 338?
3⑥2   3③8

60 is greater than 30

So 338 is less than 362.

Exercise 1D

1 Which is greater?
  (a) 184 or 162   (b) 237 or 256   (c) 439 or 476
  (d) 652 or 634   (e) 829 or 854   (f) 536 or 572

2   Which is smaller?

    (a) 694 or 647　　**(b)** 384 or 365　　**(c)** 834 or 862

    (d) 486 or 463　　**(e)** 168 or 186　　**(f)** 528 or 598

3   Put > or < in each box to make a true statement.

    (a) 248 ☐ 236　**(b)** 782 ☐ 764　**(c)** 458 ☐ 472

    (d) 234 ☐ 251　**(e)** 894 ☐ 871　**(f)** 574 ☐ 593

    (g) 653 ☐ 648　**(h)** 284 ☐ 291　**(i)** 372 ☐ 381

4   Which city is closer to London: Glasgow or Edinburgh?

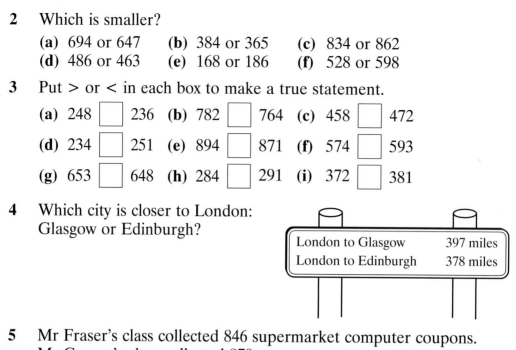

| London to Glasgow | 397 miles |
| London to Edinburgh | 378 miles |

5   Mr Fraser's class collected 846 supermarket computer coupons.
Ms Cornec's class collected 879 coupons.
Which class collected the most coupons?

6   The table shows the distance the water drops for some of the world's tallest waterfalls.

    (a) Which waterfall has the biggest drop?

    (b) Which waterfall has the smallest drop?

Name	Tugela	Mongefossen	Angel	Yosemite
Drop in metres	947	774	979	739

1.5 Mental maths

You need to be able to add and subtract numbers up to 20 in your head.
Here are three ways to work out $7 + 9$:

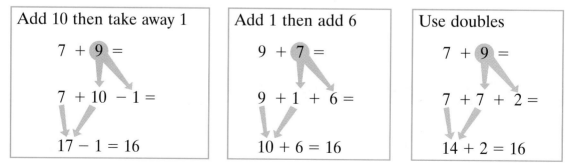

Add 10 then take away 1	Add 1 then add 6	Use doubles
$7 + 9 =$	$9 + 7 =$	$7 + 9 =$
$7 + 10 - 1 =$	$9 + 1 + 6 =$	$7 + 7 + 2 =$
$17 - 1 = 16$	$10 + 6 = 16$	$14 + 2 = 16$

Try using each of these methods for $6 + 8$.

Here are three ways to work out $14 - 8$:

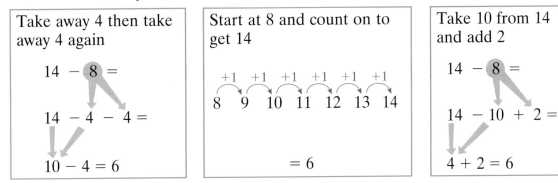

Take away 4 then take away 4 again	Start at 8 and count on to get 14	Take 10 from 14 and add 2
$14 - 8 =$ $14 - 4 - 4 =$ $10 - 4 = 6$	$+1\ +1\ +1\ +1\ +1\ +1$ $8\ \ 9\ \ 10\ \ 11\ \ 12\ \ 13\ \ 14$ $= 6$	$14 - 8 =$ $14 - 10 + 2 =$ $4 + 2 = 6$

Try using each of these methods for $16 - 9$.

You should try to use lots of different methods to see which one helps you the most.

- **Each of these words mean you should add up: total, sum, altogether, plus.**

- **Each of these words mean you should take away: minus, less, difference, subtract, . . .**

Exercise 1E

Do this exercise mentally.

1   Find as many different ways as you can to fill the square and triangular boxes.

   (a) $\square + \triangle = 10$ **(b)** $\square + 3 = \triangle$ **(c)** $5 + \square = \triangle$
   (d) $\square - \triangle = 6$ **(e)** $\square - 4 = \triangle$ **(f)** $16 - \square = \triangle$

2   These students have each chosen some numbers between 1 and 20. Find all of the possible answers for each student.

The sum of my two numbers is 12

Helen

The total of my three numbers is 9

Gary

My two numbers add up to 15

Floyd

The difference of my two numbers is 4

Joy

3 The diagram shows a route from **Start** to **Finish** through the number maze. The finishing number is $9 - 6 + 5 - 2 = 6$

(a) Find the route which gives the greatest finishing number.

(b) Find the route which gives the smallest finishing number.

(c) Make up a number maze and ask a friend to find which routes give the greatest and smallest finishing numbers.

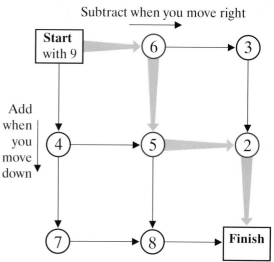

4 Activity
You need these six cards:

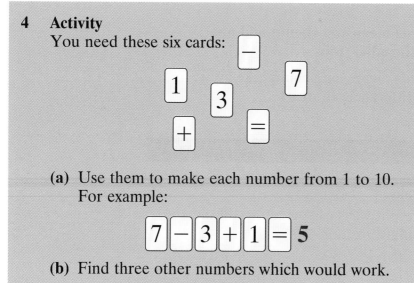

(a) Use them to make each number from 1 to 10. For example:

$$7 - 3 + 1 = 5$$

(b) Find three other numbers which would work.

You will often need to use mental maths to solve word problems.

Example 8

Naomi collects bonsai trees.
She has 8 deciduous trees and 6 evergreen trees.
How many trees does she have altogether?

She has $8 + 6 = 14$ trees altogether.

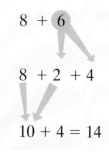

Exercise 1F

Solve these problems mentally:

1   Chen Li earns money babysitting.
    On Saturday he earns £7 and on Sunday he earns £9.
    How much does he earn in total?

2   A bookshop sells hardback books
    for £5 less than their marked prices.
    How much does each book cost?

3   Charlie bought a theatre ticket for £16.
    He paid for it with a £20 note.
    How much change did he get?

4   Gita collects old musical instruments. She has
    6 woodwind instruments, 5 brass instruments
    and 7 string instruments.
    How many instruments does she have altogether?

5   At a school fete Jessica drops three balls
    into a pinball machine.

    (a) She scores 5 with her first ball.
        What other numbers can she score
        with her next two balls to win a prize?
    (b) Find all the other ways to win a prize.

1.6 Adding and subtracting multiples of 10

■ **10, 20, 30, 40 … are called multiples of 10**
   They are the answers in the 10 times multiplication
   table

these are the
multiples of 10
↓
$1 \times 10 = 10$
$2 \times 10 = 20$
$3 \times 10 = 30$
⋮   ⋮   ⋮

Example 9

Work out $30 + 20$.

Think of $3 + 2 = 5$:

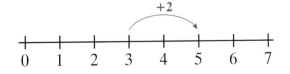

Now make all the numbers 10 times bigger:

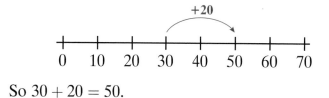

+20

So $30 + 20 = 50$.

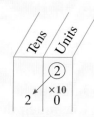

Remember:
To multiply by ten
move the digits one
place to the left and
put zero in the units
column.

Exercise 1G

Work these out mentally

1   (a) $40 + 20$ (b) $30 + 40$ (c) $20 + 60$ (d) $70 + 20$
    (e) $60 + 30$ (f) $10 + 80$ (g) $50 + 40$ (h) $20 + 50$

2   (a) $80 - 30$ (b) $60 - 40$ (c) $70 - 20$ (d) $90 - 30$
    (e) $50 - 20$ (f) $40 - 30$ (g) $80 - 60$ (h) $70 - 40$

3   (a) $50 + 30$ (b) $80 - 50$ (c) $50 + 20$ (d) $90 - 20$
    (e) $70 - 30$ (f) $60 - 30$ (g) $50 - 30$ (h) $40 + 60$

4   (a) $80 + 60$ (b) $70 + 50$ (c) $90 + 40$
    (d) $40 + 30 + 50$ (e) $80 + 70 + 20$ (f) $60 + 70 - 20$
    (g) $70 + 80 - 30$ (h) $90 + 70 - 20$ (i) $80 + 50 - 70$

5   (a) $120 - 40$ (b) $160 - 90$ (c) $150 - 70$
    (d) $130 - 60$ (e) $80 + 40 - 30$ (f) $90 + 30 - 50$
    (g) $70 + 80 - 90$ (h) $60 + 60 - 30$ (i) $110 - 20 + 60$

1.7 Rounding to the nearest 10

Shareen, Bill and Helena are planning
a party. Altogether they have invited
about $40 + 50 + 50 = 140$ people.
They all rounded their numbers to
the nearest 10.

Shareen

Helena

I've invited
about 50
people

I've invited
about 40
people

Bill

I've invited
about 50 people
too

■ **To round to the nearest 10:**
Look at the digit in the units column.
If it is less than 5 then you round down.
If it is 5 or more then you round up.

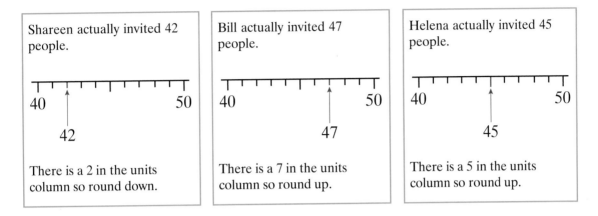

Shareen actually invited 42 people.	Bill actually invited 47 people.	Helena actually invited 45 people.
There is a 2 in the units column so round down.	There is a 7 in the units column so round up.	There is a 5 in the units column so round up.

Example 10

Find an approximate answer for:

(a) 48 + 32   (b) 75 + 51

Hint: Approximate means 'about the same'.

Round each number to the nearest 10 then add.

(a) 48 rounds up to   50
     32 rounds down to   30 +
                                        80

So 48 + 32 is about 80.

(b) 75 rounds up to   80
     51 rounds down to   50 +
                                       130

So 75 + 51 is about 130.

Exercise 1H

1   Round each of these numbers to the nearest 10.

   (a) 37   (b) 52   (c) 29   (d) 3

   (e) 56   (f) 5   (g) 74   (h) 65

   (i) 18   (j) 95   (k) 14   (l) 98

Hint: A number less than five rounds down to zero.

2   Approximate each of these numbers to the nearest 10.

   (a) 132   (b) 157   (c) 169   (d) 271

   (e) 364   (f) 235   (g) 429   (h) 382

   (i) 497   (j) 244   (k) 392   (l) 798

Hint: Approximate means the same as round.

3   Round each number to the nearest 10 then add or
subtract to find an approximate answer.

    (a) $28 + 51$ **(b)** $32 + 49$ **(c)** $23 + 42$ **(d)** $57 + 27$
    (e) $45 + 21$ **(f)** $28 + 51$ **(g)** $43 + 58$ **(h)** $36 + 63$
    (i) $83 - 29$ **(j)** $78 - 32$ **(k)** $91 - 48$ **(l)** $43 - 21$
    (m) $97 - 34$ **(n)** $85 - 29$ **(o)** $53 - 35$ **(p)** $82 - 48$

4   Find an approximate answer.

    (a) $89 + 31$ **(b)** $72 + 57$ **(c)** $85 + 36$ **(d)** $78 + 45$
    (e) $68 + 75$ **(f)** $98 + 41$ **(g)** $67 + 38$ **(h)** $85 + 38$

1.8 Adding and subtracting multiples of 100

■   **100, 200, 300, 400 ...... are called multiples of 100**
They are the answers in the 100 times multiplication
table

To do $300 + 200$

Think of $3 + 2 = 5$:

Now make all the numbers
100 times bigger:

So $300 + 200 = 500$

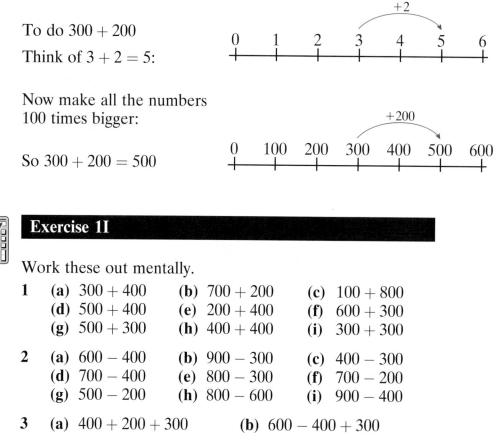

Exercise 1I

Work these out mentally.

1   **(a)** $300 + 400$ **(b)** $700 + 200$ **(c)** $100 + 800$
    (d) $500 + 400$ **(e)** $200 + 400$ **(f)** $600 + 300$
    (g) $500 + 300$ **(h)** $400 + 400$ **(i)** $300 + 300$

2   **(a)** $600 - 400$ **(b)** $900 - 300$ **(c)** $400 - 300$
    (d) $700 - 400$ **(e)** $800 - 300$ **(f)** $700 - 200$
    (g) $500 - 200$ **(h)** $800 - 600$ **(i)** $900 - 400$

3   **(a)** $400 + 200 + 300$ **(b)** $600 - 400 + 300$
    (c) $800 - 200 - 400$ **(d)** $700 - 500 + 300$
    (e) $200 + 700 - 400$ **(f)** $500 + 300 - 100$
    (g) $600 - 300 + 600$ **(h)** $800 + 100 - 900$

1.9 Rounding to the nearest 100

Shareen, Bill and Helena have been collecting coupons for a computer. Altogether they have collected about $200 + 300 + 300 = 800$ coupons. They all rounded their numbers to the nearest 100.

■   **To round to the nearest 100:**
Look at the digit in the tens column.
If it is less than 5 then you round down.
If it is 5 or more then you round up.

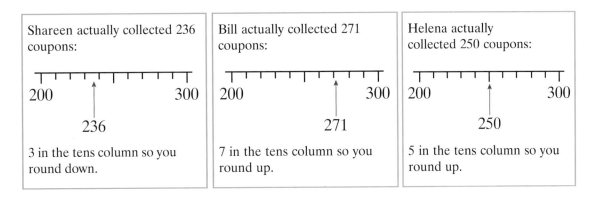

Shareen actually collected 236 coupons:	Bill actually collected 271 coupons:	Helena actually collected 250 coupons:
200 ——— 300	200 ——— 300	200 ——— 300
236	271	250
3 in the tens column so you round down.	7 in the tens column so you round up.	5 in the tens column so you round up.

Example 11

Find an approximate answer for $473 + 312$

$473 + 312$ is about $500 + 300$:

473 rounds to 500   Round each number to
312 rounds to 300 +   the nearest hundred …
⎯⎯⎯
800   … then add.

So $473 + 312$ is about 800.

Exercise 1J

1   Round each of these numbers to the nearest 100.

(a) 317   (b) 528   (c) 293   (d) 473
(e) 850   (f) 835   (g) 874   (h) 652
(i) 180   (j) 905   (k) 140   (l) 918

2 Approximate each of these numbers to the nearest 100.

    (a) 132   **(b)** 157   **(c)** 169   **(d)** 271
    (e) 364   **(f)** 235   **(g)** 429   **(h)** 382
    (i) 497   **(j)** 244   **(k)** 392   **(l)** 798

3 Round each number to the nearest 100 then add to find an approximate answer.

    (a) $248 + 516$ **(b)** $382 + 494$ **(c)** $234 + 423$
    (d) $567 + 207$ **(e)** $425 + 213$ **(f)** $248 + 651$
    (g) $483 + 338$ **(h)** $316 + 603$ **(i)** $172 + 649$

4 Round each number to the nearest 100 then subtract to find an approximate answer.

    (a) $893 - 290$ **(b)** $748 - 321$ **(c)** $941 - 483$
    (d) $435 - 251$ **(e)** $971 - 348$ **(f)** $855 - 259$
    (g) $563 - 365$ **(h)** $802 - 480$ **(i)** $781 - 493$

1.10 Checking answers by estimation

You can use rounding to check if an answer is correct.

37 rounded to the nearest 10 is 40
26 rounded to the nearest 10 is 30
So $37 + 26$ is about
      $40 + 30$
      $= 70$

£93 is much too big so it must be wrong.

Example 12

Find the correct answer to $29 + 43$ from the cloud.

Round each number to the nearest 10:

    29 rounds to 30
    43 rounds to $\underline{40} +$
              $\overline{70}$

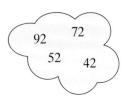

So 72 must be the correct answer.

Example 13

Which calculator shows the correct answer to
349 + 263?

Round each number to the nearest 100:
349 + 263 is about 300 + 300 =
$$600$$

So calculator B shows the correct answer of 612.

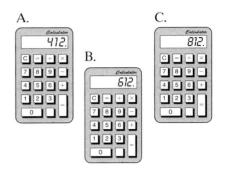

Exercise 1K

1   Each box can only be opened by the key with the
correct answer on it.
Say which key will open each box by finding an
approximate answer to each question.

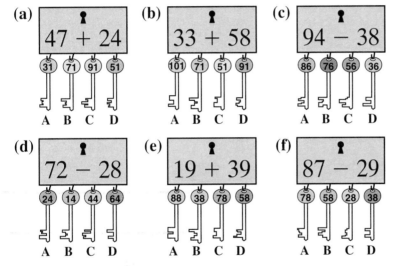

(a) 47 + 24
31 (A) 71 (B) 91 (C) 51 (D)

(b) 33 + 58
101 (A) 71 (B) 51 (C) 91 (D)

(c) 94 − 38
86 (A) 76 (B) 56 (C) 36 (D)

(d) 72 − 28
24 (A) 14 (B) 44 (C) 64 (D)

(e) 19 + 39
88 (A) 38 (B) 78 (C) 58 (D)

(f) 87 − 29
78 (A) 58 (B) 28 (C) 38 (D)

2   Find an approximate answer to each calculation then
choose which calculator shows the correct answer.

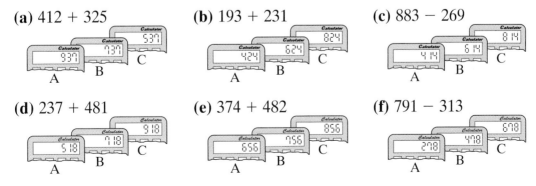

(a) 412 + 325
A 930   B 737   C 537

(b) 193 + 231
A 424   B 624   C 824

(c) 883 − 269
A 414   B 614   C 814

(d) 237 + 481
A 518   B 718   C 918

(e) 374 + 482
A 656   B 756   C 856

(f) 791 − 313
A 278   B 478   C 678

1.11 Adding and subtracting a multiple of 10 to a 2-digit number

■ When you add or subtract a multiple of 10 to a 2-digit number the units digit does not change.

Example 14

Work out $56 + 30$

Think of $50 + 30 = 80$:

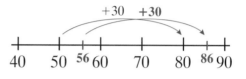

The units digit does not change so:

$$50 + 30 = 80$$

and $56 + 30 = 86$

Example 15

Work out $78 - 30$

Think of $70 - 30 = 40$:

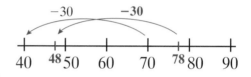

The units digit does not change so:

$$70 - 30 = 40$$

and $78 - 30 = 48$

Exercise 1L

1 (a) $37 + 10$ (b) $42 + 20$ (c) $63 + 10$
  (d) $79 + 20$ (e) $48 + 40$ (f) $56 + 30$

2 (a) $42 - 10$ (b) $62 - 20$ (c) $78 - 10$
  (d) $44 - 30$ (e) $39 - 20$ (f) $95 - 60$

3 (a) $78 + 60$ (b) $83 + 40$ (c) $91 + 30$
  (d) $59 + 70$ (e) $98 + 50$ (f) $86 + 70$

4 (a) $167 - 40$ (b) $156 - 20$ (c) $183 - 50$
  (d) $138 - 20$ (e) $123 - 50$ (f) $117 - 30$

5 (a) $27 + 20 + 30$ (b) $43 + 40 + 10$ (c) $96 - 30 - 20$
  (d) $87 - 50 - 20$ (e) $78 - 40 - 30$ (f) $9 + 60 + 20$

6 (a) $76 - 10 + 20$ (b) $51 - 20 + 30$ (c) $29 - 20 + 80$
  (d) $39 + 60 - 20$ (e) $47 + 50 - 30$ (f) $74 - 60 + 20$

7 **(a)** $89 + 50 - 20$ **(b)** $97 + 60 - 30$
    (c) $76 + 60 - 10$ **(d)** $87 + 90 - 60$
    (e) $148 - 60 + 10$ **(f)** $136 - 90 + 20$
    (g) $143 - 80 + 30$ **(h)** $159 - 60 + 20$

1.12 Mental maths with 2-digit numbers

This section show you how to add and subtract 2-digit numbers in your head.

Here are two ways to do $48 + 26$:

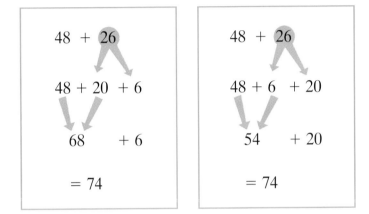

Here are three ways to do $63 - 27$:

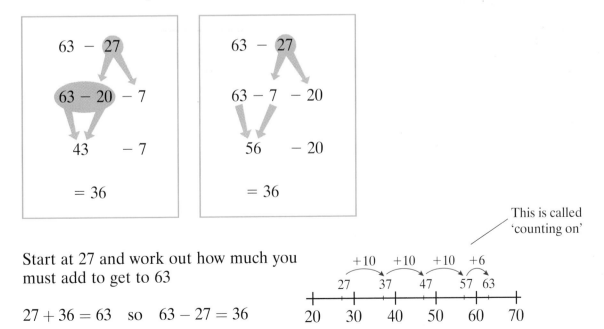

This is called 'counting on'

Start at 27 and work out how much you must add to get to 63

$27 + 36 = 63$ so $63 - 27 = 36$

You can use a similar method for numbers that go over 100:

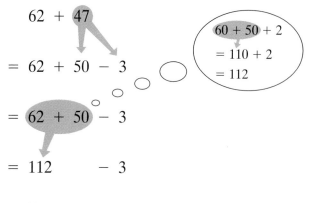

$$= 62 + 50 - 3$$

$$= 62 + 50 - 3$$

$$= 112 \quad\quad - 3$$

$$= 109$$

This works for larger numbers too:

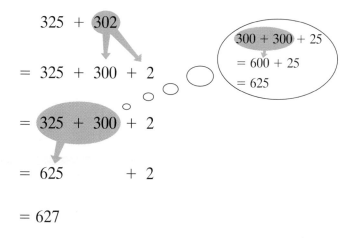

$$= 325 + 300 + 2$$

$$= 325 + 300 + 2$$

$$= 625 \quad\quad + 2$$

$$= 627$$

Exercise 1M

Show how you would work these out mentally:

1 (a) $15 + 58$ (b) $46 + 82$ (c) $150 + 297$

Hint: draw diagrams to help show your method.

You should work all these answers out mentally.

2 (a) $35 + 21$ (b) $26 + 23$ (c) $46 + 31$
   (d) $43 + 25$ (e) $24 + 63$ (f) $14 + 72$
   (g) $55 + 13$ (h) $64 + 34$ (i) $56 + 32$

3 (a) $28 + 14$ (b) $39 + 25$ (c) $57 + 27$
   (d) $48 + 13$ (e) $26 + 45$ (f) $48 + 43$
   (g) $62 + 29$ (h) $64 + 26$ (i) $55 + 28$

4 (a) $73 + 49$ (b) $69 + 38$ (c) $87 + 59$
(d) $86 + 47$ (e) $436 + 203$ (f) $345 + 402$
(g) $684 + 203$ (h) $307 + 641$ (i) $205 + 493$

5 (a) $36 - 12$ (b) $46 - 13$ (c) $57 - 24$
(d) $63 - 21$ (e) $58 - 34$ (f) $74 - 43$
(g) $96 - 54$ (h) $87 - 43$ (i) $79 - 53$
(j) $86 - 52$ (k) $94 - 73$ (l) $86 - 43$

6 (a) $35 - 16$ (b) $42 - 25$ (c) $54 - 34$
(d) $64 - 25$ (e) $47 - 29$ (f) $66 - 37$
(g) $73 - 35$ (h) $86 - 47$ (i) $93 - 56$
(j) $78 - 29$ (k) $94 - 28$ (l) $86 - 28$

7 In a T.V. Quiz Game contestants have to guess the price of an antique.

Whose guess was nearest for each antique?

Antique	Price
Clock	£78
Vase	£47
Mirror	£59
Jug	£34

(a) **Clock:**
  Shamus £86
  Tom £63
  Mike £59

(b) **Vase:**
  Shamus £72
  Tom £56
  Mike £39

(c) **Mirror:**
  Shamus £45
  Tom £84
  Mike £71

(d) **Jug:**
  Shamus £44
  Tom £27
  Mike £45

8 The table shows the scores of four pupils in two Maths tests:

(a) What is the total score for each pupil?
(b) What is the difference between the highest and lowest scores in Maths1?
(c) What is the difference between the highest and lowest scores in Maths2?
(d) What is the difference between the highest and lowest total scores?

Name	Maths1	Maths2
Helena	35	48
Josie	27	36
Bill	29	32
Shareen	46	47

9 Elaine, Amy and Winston have been shopping.

(a) How much did Elaine spend in total?
(b) Winston paid with a £50 note. How much change did he get?
(c) Amy only had £40. How much money did she have to borrow to pay for her shopping?

Elaine: I bought a blouse for £28 and a skirt for £34

Amy: I bought shoes for £36 and a bag for £18

Winston: I bought a shirt for £27

1.13 Adding numbers on paper

This section shows you how to add any large numbers on paper:
To do 954 + 678:

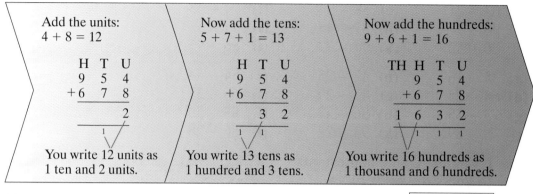

Add the units:	Now add the tens:	Now add the hundreds:
4 + 8 = 12	5 + 7 + 1 = 13	9 + 6 + 1 = 16

```
  H  T  U
  9  5  4
+ 6  7  8
        2
     1
```

```
  H  T  U
  9  5  4
+ 6  7  8
     3  2
  1  1
```

```
TH H  T  U
   9  5  4
 + 6  7  8
 1 6  3  2
   1  1  1
```

You write 12 units as 1 ten and 2 units.

You write 13 tens as 1 hundred and 3 tens.

You write 16 hundreds as 1 thousand and 6 hundreds.

You can use the same method to do sums like
2147 + 35 + 461:

```
Th H T U
 2  1 4 7
      3 5
    4 6 1
 2  6 4 3
    1 1
```

Remember to line up the units

Exercise 1N

1   Work out:

(a) 243 + 435   (b) 147 + 35
(c) 356 + 233   (d) 428 + 136
(e) 46 + 12 + 25   (f) 568 + 2154
(g) 336 + 48 + 35   (h) 786 + 547 + 2461
(i) 2465 + 27   (j) 1847 + 7892

2   The table shows the number of
    CDs sold by a shop during a
    week in September.

(a) What was the total number
    of CDs sold on Monday,
    Tuesday and Wednesday?
(b) What was the total number
    of CDs sold on Thursday
    and Friday?
(c) What was the total number
    of CDs sold at the weekend?

Week beginning 18th September	
Monday	74
Tuesday	38
Wednesday	52
Thursday	37
Friday	344
Saturday	669
Sunday	458

1.14 Subtracting numbers on paper

To do 728 − 257:

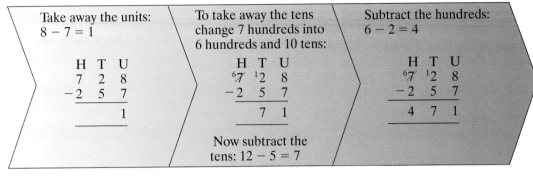

Take away the units:
8 − 7 = 1

```
  H  T  U
  7  2  8
− 2  5  7
        1
```

To take away the tens
change 7 hundreds into
6 hundreds and 10 tens:

```
    H   T  U
   ⁶7  ¹2  8
 − 2   5   7
       7   1
```

Now subtract the
tens: 12 − 5 = 7

Subtract the hundreds:
6 − 2 = 4

```
    H   T  U
   ⁶7  ¹2  8
 − 2   5   7
   4   7   1
```

You can use the same method to do subtractions like
836 − 57.

```
   H   T  U
  ⁷8 ¹²3̸ ¹6
 −     5  7
   7   7  9
```

Remember to
line up the units

Exercise 1O

1 Work out:

(a) 576 − 432
(b) 597 − 243
(c) 765 − 349
(d) 867 − 348
(e) 84 − 38
(f) 745 − 367
(g) 475 − 23
(h) 654 − 29
(i) 546 − 87
(j) 604 − 237

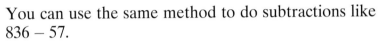

Hint: Change the
6 hundreds into
5 hundreds and
10 tens

2 By how much has the price of each appliance
been reduced in this sale?

Appliance	Normal Price	Sale Price
Toaster	£64	£38
Microwave	£125	£87
Dishwasher	£484	£355
Washing machine	£572	£394
Cooker	£706	£438

3 Two auctioners, Arthur and Dale, each estimated the sale prices of some furniture. Their estimates and the actual sale price are shown in the table. For each piece of furniture whose estimate was nearest?

Item	Arthur's estimate	Dale's estimate	Actual Price £
Chest	178	256	225
Wardrobe	478	393	425
Chair	389	276	343
Table	896	974	932

Summary of key points

1 The value of a digit depends on its place in the number:

	Hundreds	Tens	Units	
3 hundreds = 300	(3)	8	2	Three hundred and eighty two
3 tens = 30	8	(3)	2	Eight hundred and thirty two
3 units = 3	2	8	(3)	Two hundred and eighty three

2 382 is a three-digit number. 38 is a two-digit number.

3 A place value diagram can help you to read large numbers:
The digit 7 means:

	Millions	Hundred thousands	Ten thousands	Thousands	Hundreds	Tens	Units	
7 thousands				(7)	0	0	0	Seven thousand
7 ten thousands			(7)	0	0	0	0	Seventy thousand
7 hundred thousands		(7)	0	0	0	0	0	Seven hundred thousand
7 millions	(7)	0	0	0	0	0	0	Seven million

4 The digit with the highest place value is on the left of the number.

5 Each of these words means you should add up: total, sum, altogether, plus, . . .

6 Each of these words means you should take away: minus, less difference, subtract, ...

7 10, 20, 30, 40, . . . are called the multiples of 10.
They are the numbers in the 10 times multiplication table.

8 To round to the nearest 10:
Look at the digit in the units column –
If it is less than 5 then you round down
If it is 5 or more then you round up.

9 100, 200, 300, 400, . . . are called multiples of 100.
They are the numbers in the 100 times multiplication table.

10 To round to the nearest hundred:
Look at the digit in the tens column –
If it is less than 5 then you round down
If it is 5 or more then you round up.

11 When you add or subtract a multiple of 10 to a 2-digit number the units digit does not change.

2 Symmetry and angles

2.1 Symmetrical shapes

This leaf has reflective symmetry:

It has one line of symmetry:

If you put a mirror on the line ...

... the leaf looks the same.

Example 1

Draw in all the lines of symmetry on these shapes:

(a) **(b)** **(c)**

(a) **(b)** **(c)**

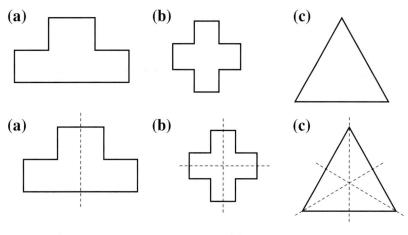

This shape has **rotational symmetry**:

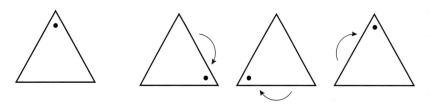

The shape looks the same three times in one full turn. You say that the shape has rotational symmetry of order 3.

It looks the same three times in one full turn.

■ **A shape has rotational symmetry if it looks exactly the same after a rotation.**

Exercise 2A

1 For each shape:
   - Say whether it has reflective symmetry.
   - If it has, copy it and draw in all the lines of symmetry.

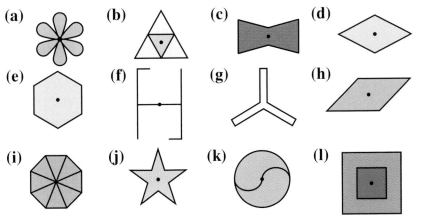

2 Say which of these shapes have rotational symmetry.

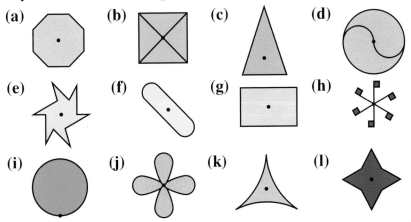

   For each shape with rotational symmetry, say what the order is.

3 Copy and complete each shape by drawing the reflection in the line of symmetry.

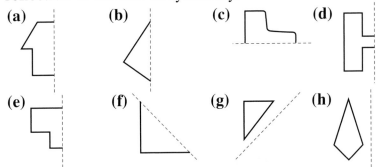

   Which of the finished shapes have rotational symmetry?

4 Copy and complete these shapes by drawing the reflection in each line of symmetry:

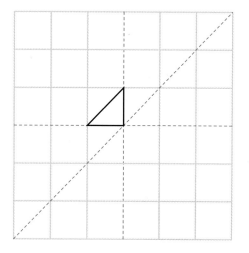

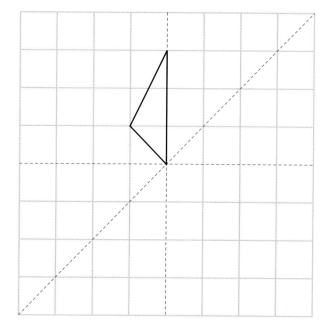

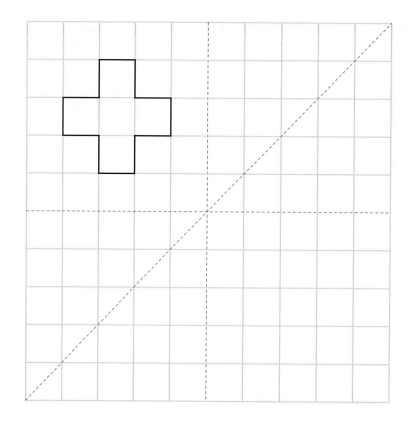

2.2 Measuring turns

A rotation is a turn.

■ **You can measure turns using degrees, ° for short:**

There are 90° in a quarter turn.   There are 180° in a half turn.   There are 360 degrees (360°) in a full turn.

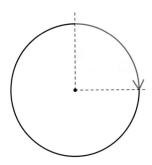
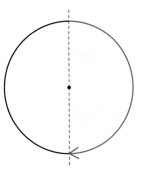
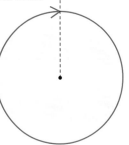

Example 2

This compass needle points North.
What direction will it be pointing in after a rotation of:

(a) 90° clockwise   **(b)** 180°   **(c)** 90° anticlockwise

(a) East.
(b) This is a half turn so the needle will point South.
(c) West.

Exercise 2B

1   Where will the compass needle point after:

(a) a half turn from East
(b) a quarter turn clockwise from South West
(c) a quarter turn anticlockwise from South
(d) a full turn from North West
(e) a quarter turn clockwise from North East
(f) a half turn from South.

2   For **(a)** to **(h)** say:

● What turn is needed to get from the first to the second point?

● How many degrees are in each turn

(a) F to H   **(b)** A to E   **(c)** B to H
(d) C to G   **(e)** F to B   **(f)** B to D?

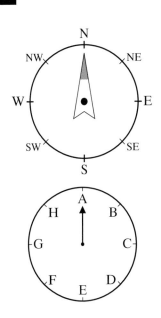

2.3 Angle types

■ **Certain types of angles have different names:**

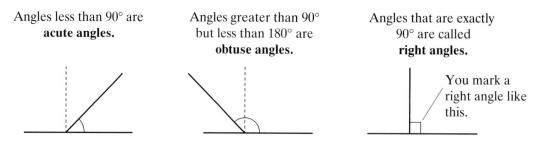

Angles less than 90° are **acute angles.**

Angles greater than 90° but less than 180° are **obtuse angles.**

Angles that are exactly 90° are called **right angles.**

You mark a right angle like this.

Example 3

State the angle type of each of these angles.

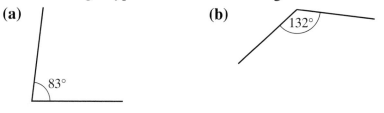

(a)

(b) 132°

83°

(a) Less than 90° so acute.　(b) Between 90° and 180° so obtuse.

Exercise 2C

1　Without measuring, write down the angle type of these angles.

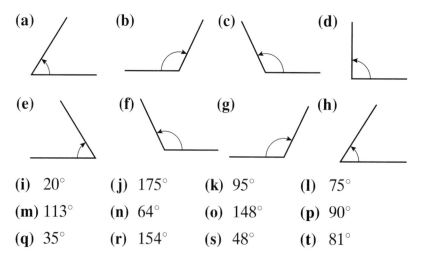

(a) (b) (c) (d)

(e) (f) (g) (h)

(i)　20°　　(j)　175°　　(k)　95°　　(l)　75°

(m) 113°　　(n)　64°　　(o)　148°　　(p)　90°

(q)　35°　　(r)　154°　　(s)　48°　　(t)　81°

2.4 Measuring angles

You can use a protractor to measure angles:

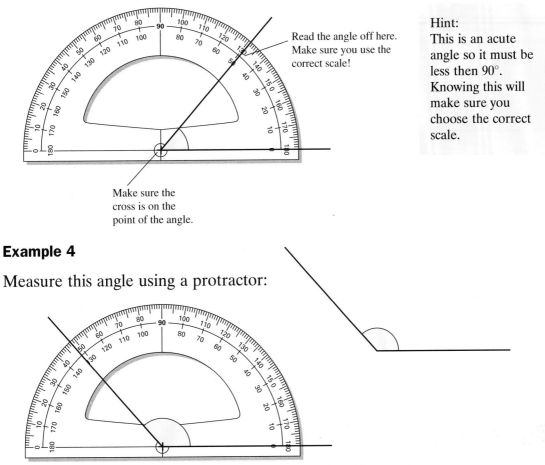

Read the angle off here.
Make sure you use the
correct scale!

Make sure the
cross is on the
point of the angle.

Hint:
This is an acute
angle so it must be
less then 90°.
Knowing this will
make sure you
choose the correct
scale.

Example 4

Measure this angle using a protractor:

The line goes through the mark for 48° and 132°. The angle
is obtuse so the answer must be 132°.

Exercise 2D

1 For each of these angles:
   • Measure the angle using a protractor.
   • State the angle type.

   (a)   **(b)**   **(c)**

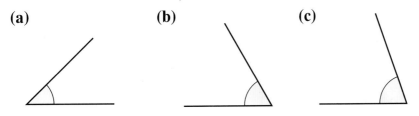

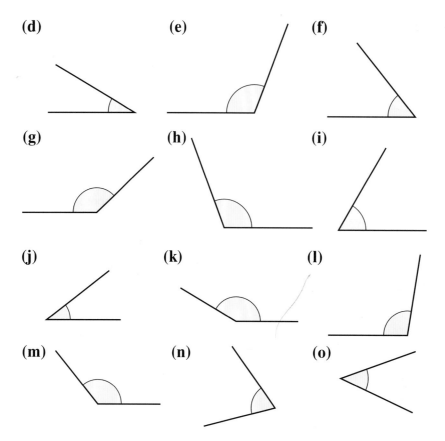

2.5 Drawing angles

You can also use a protractor to draw angles:

To draw an angle of 53°:

Draw a line.   Put the protractor on   Make a mark at   Complete and mark
the line like this: 53°.   the angle:

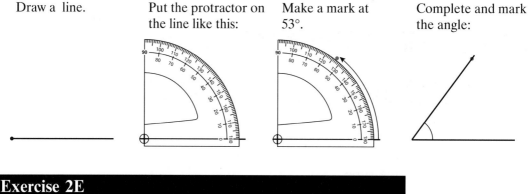

Exercise 2E

1   Draw these angles using a protractor.

(a) 70°   (b) 170°   (c) 115°   (d) 20°
(e) 145°   (f) 35°   (g) 65°   (h) 96°
(i) 48°   (j) 123°   (k) 152°   (l) 17°

2.6 Estimating angles

You can estimate the size of an angle by comparing it to a right angle.

Example 5

Estimate the size of each of these angles:

(a)

(b)

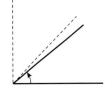

(a) This angle is just less than half a right angle.

Half a right angle is $45°$ so a good estimate for the size of the angle is $40°$.

The actual angle is $38°$.

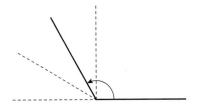

(b) This angle is a right angle plus $\frac{1}{3}$.

$\frac{1}{3}$ of a right angle is $30°$ so the angle is about $90° + 30° = 120°$

Exercise 2F

1 For each angle:
 • Write down the angle type.
 • Estimate the size of the angle.

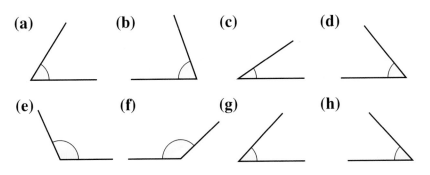

(a) (b) (c) (d)

(e) (f) (g) (h)

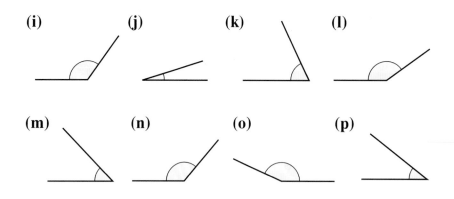

(i)   **(j)**   **(k)**   **(l)**

(m)   **(n)**   **(o)**   **(p)**

2.7 Angles on lines

You can use the properties of a right angle or straight line to work out the size of a missing angle.

- **Angles which make a right angle add to 90°**

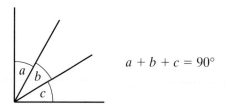

$a + b + c = 90°$

- **Angles which make a straight line add to 180°**

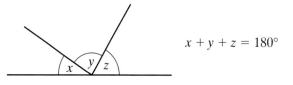

$x + y + z = 180°$

Example 6

Work out the size of the missing angles.

(a)   **(b)**

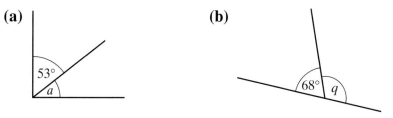

(a) The two angles add to 90° so $a = 37°$

(b) The two angles add to 180° so $q = 112°$

Exercise 2G

1 In each question find the value of the letter.

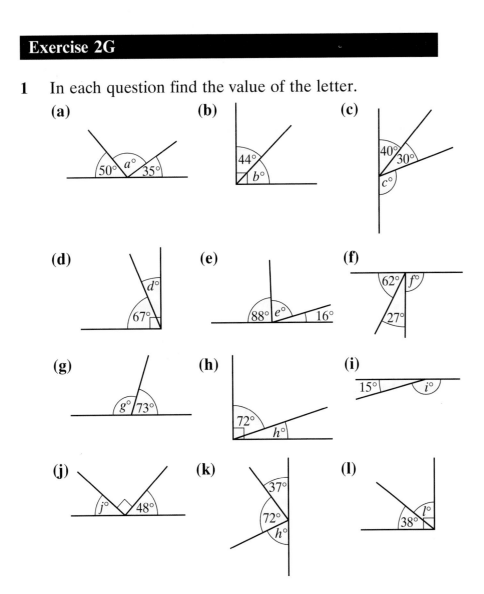

(a)

(b)

(c)

(d)

(e)

(f)

(g)

(h)

(i)

(j)

(k)

(l)

2.8 Angles at a point

A full turn is $360°$.

■ **Angles in a circle add to $360°$.**

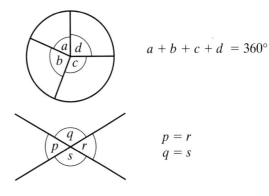

$a + b + c + d = 360°$

■ **When two straight lines cross the opposite angles are equal.**

$p = r$
$q = s$

Example 7

Ashley cuts a cake like this:

What is the size of the missing slice?

The other slices add up to

$23 + 68 + 97 + 59 = 247°$

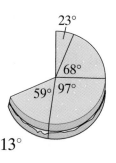

The missing slice measures $360 - 247 = 113°$

He cuts another cake like this:

How many degrees is slice x?

x must be the same size as the top slice because the two cuts are straight lines. So x must measure $140°$.

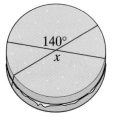

Exercise 2H

1   In each question find the value of the letter.

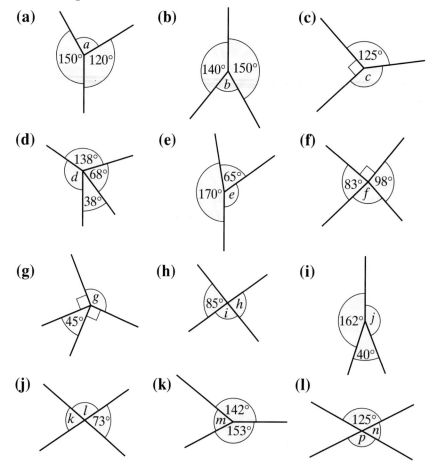

(a)

(b)

(c)

(d)

(e)

(f)

(g)

(h)

(i)

(j)

(k)

(l)

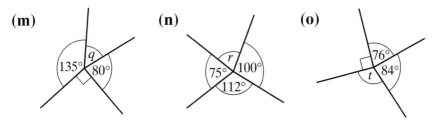

(m) **(n)** **(o)**

2.9 Angles in shapes

Sometimes you need to name angles in diagrams.
You can do this in two ways:

By using a single letter ... ... or by using points

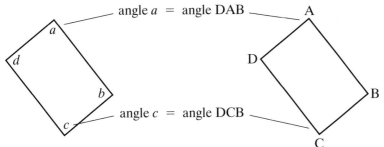

angle a = angle DAB

angle c = angle DCB

Example 8

Write down:

(a) Angle x using points

(b) Angle QSR as a single letter

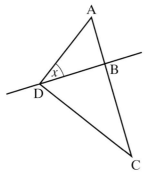

(a) x = angle ADB

(b) Angle QSR = g

Exercise 2I

1 Use points to describe the angle shaded in each diagram.

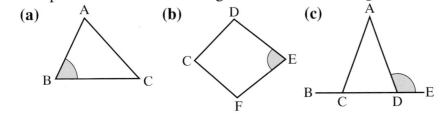

(a) **(b)** **(c)**

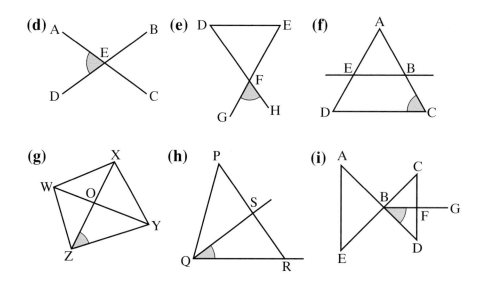

2 Write down the single letter which shows the angle given by the points.

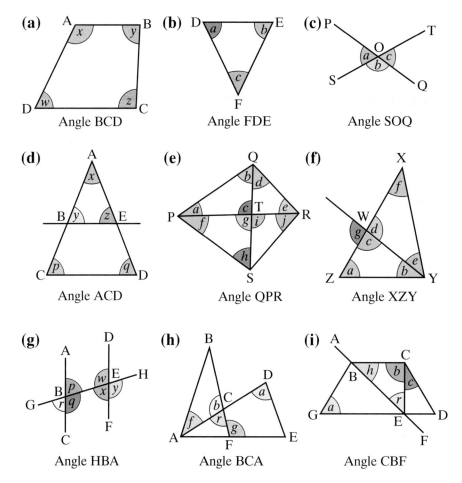

2.10 Angles in a triangle

Activity

- Draw a triangle on a piece of paper.
- Cut out the triangle and tear it into three like this:
- Put the pieces together:

The three angles together make a straight line.
This works for any triangle.

■ **The angles of a triangle always add to 180°.**

Example 9

How many degrees is angle x ?

The three angles add to 180°.

$x = 180 - 36 - 57 = 87°$.

So x must measure 87°.

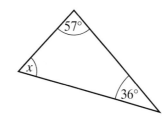

Exercise 2J

1 Find the missing angle in each triangle.

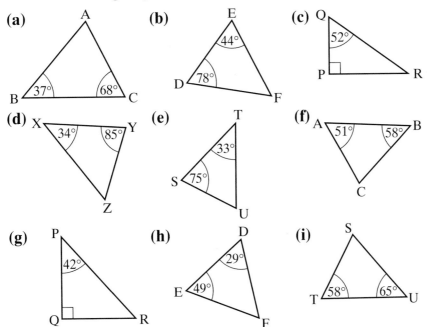

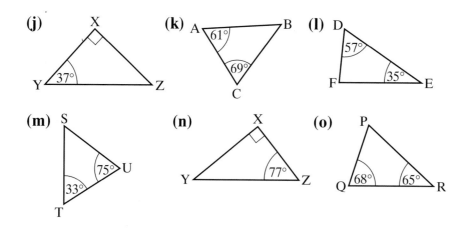

(j) X Y 37° Z

(k) A 61° B C 69°

(l) D 57° F 35° E

(m) S T 33° U 75°

(n) X Y 77° Z

(o) P Q 68° 65° R

Summary of key points

1 A shape has rotational symmetry if it looks exactly the same after a rotation.

2 You can measure turns using degrees, ° for short.

3 Certain types of angles have different names:

Angles less than 90° are **acute angles.**

Angles greater than 90° but less than 180° are **obtuse angles.**

Angles that are exactly 90° are called **right angles.**

You mark a right angle like this.

4 Angles which make a right angle add to 90°

5 Angles which make a straight line add to 180°.

6 Angles in a circle add to 360°.

7 When two straight lines cross the opposite angles are equal.

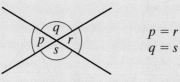

$p = r$
$q = s$

8 The angles of a triangle always add to 180°.

3 Multiplication and division

This chapter will help you develop your multiplication and division skills.

3.1 Multiplication up to 10 × 10

It is important that you learn your multiplication tables up to 10 × 10. Exercise 3A will give you practise in using them.

5 x £3 = £15 altogether

Exercise 3A

1 **Activity** You need a watch or clock with a seconds hand.
Draw a 5 by 5 multiplication square like this:

- Write five numbers in any order along the top
- Write the same numbers in a different order down the side
- Time how long it takes to fill in the rest of the square

Make sure you check your answers!

Draw another square and put the numbers along the top and side in a different order. Try and beat your time to fill in the square.

Repeat the activity with five different numbers.

×	7	5	9	3	8
3					
9					
7					
5			45		
8					

5 × 9 = 45

2 The diagram shows a 3 by 3 multiplication square.
   (a) Find the missing numbers
   (b) Make up your own grid and try it on a friend.

×	4		
3		21	
		28	
7			21

3 For each 2 by 2 multiplication square:
   (a) Write in the answers.
   (b) Find the total of the answers.

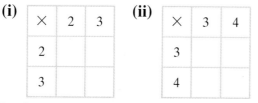

   (i)

×	2	3
2		
3		

   (ii)

×	3	4
3		
4		

   (c) Make up some of your own to solve.
      What do you notice about your answers?

4 **(a)** Find a 2 by 2 multiplication square in which the
      answers total:
      (i) 36 **(ii)** 64 **(iii)** 81 **(iv)** 49
   (b) Find a 3 by 3 multiplication square in which the
      answers total:
      (i) 81 **(ii)** 100

5 Write four numbers in a 2 by 2 grid.

   Multiply the numbers on each side of the
   grid and add to find the total:

   $2 \times 5 = 10$

   $2 \times 3 = 6$

2	5
3	4

   $5 \times 4 = 20$

   $3 \times 4 = 12$

   ```
   10
   20
   12
    6 +
   ___
   48
   ```

   Try other ways of putting the numbers in the grid.
   What is the biggest total you can make?

   Try other sets of four numbers.
   What do you notice about your results?

6 **(a)** Write down any pair of numbers which add up to 9.
      Multiply the numbers together.

      $7 + 2 = 9$
      $7 \times 2 = 14$

      Do the same for other pairs of numbers which
      add up to 9.
      Which pair of numbers gives the largest answer
      when you multiply them together?

      $3 + 6 = 9$
      $3 \times 6 = 18$

   (b) Do the same for numbers other than 9
   (c) What do you notice?
   (d) Do the same for triples of numbers which add up
      to 9.

      $2 + 3 + 4 = 9$
      $2 \times 3 \times 4 = 24$

3.2 **Dividing**

Brenda Baker makes 18 cakes.

She puts them in boxes of 6. She fills 3 boxes.  You write $18 \div 6 = 3$.	3 friends buy the cakes. They each get 6 cakes.  You write $18 \div 3 = 6$.

You can think of $18 \div 6$ in lots of ways:

    18 divided by 6
    Share 18 between 6
    How many sixes are there in 18?

■ **Division is the opposite of multiplication**
   $3 \times 6 = 18$ so $18 \div 6 = 3$
              and $18 \div 3 = 6$

Example 1

Work out $27 \div 9$
$3 \times 9 = 27$ so $27 \div 9 = 3$

Think of the 9 times
multiplication table.
$1 \times 9 = 9$
$2 \times 9 = 18$
$3 \times 9 = 27$ so **$27 \div 9 = 3$**
$4 \times 9 = 36$
. . . .

Example 2

Work out the missing numbers:

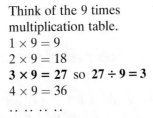

The number in the middle is
the answer to all the divisions.

$4 \div \square = 2$ so $\square = 4 \div 2$
          and $\square = 2$

$\square \div 5 = 2$ so $\square = 2 \times 5$
       and $\square = 10$

$16 \div \square = 2$ so $\square = 16 \div 2$
          and $\square = 8$

$14 \div \square = 2$ so $\square = 14 \div 2$
       and $\square = 7$

Remember:
    $14 \div 2 = 7$
so, $14 \div 7 = 2$

Exercise 3B

You should work these out mentally:

1   (a) $14 \div 2$ (b) $24 \div 4$ (c) $18 \div 3$ (d) $21 \div 3$
    (e) $36 \div 4$ (f) $16 \div 2$ (g) $40 \div 4$ (h) $24 \div 3$
    (i) $20 \div 2$ (j) $15 \div 3$ (k) $28 \div 4$ (l) $20 \div 4$

2   (a) $20 \div 5$ (b) $18 \div 6$ (c) $35 \div 5$ (d) $21 \div 7$
    (e) $24 \div 6$ (f) $42 \div 7$ (g) $45 \div 5$ (h) $35 \div 7$
    (i) $54 \div 6$ (j) $56 \div 7$ (k) $30 \div 5$ (l) $36 \div 6$

3   (a) $24 \div 8$ (b) $40 \div 8$ (c) $27 \div 9$ (d) $50 \div 10$
    (e) $56 \div 8$ (f) $45 \div 9$ (g) $70 \div 10$ (h) $32 \div 8$
    (i) $63 \div 9$ (j) $81 \div 9$ (k) $72 \div 9$ (l) $64 \div 8$

4   Find the numbers missing from each box. The number
    in the middle is the answer to all the divisions.

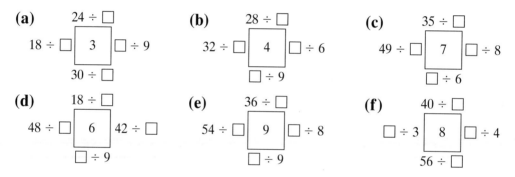

(a) $24 \div \square$
    $18 \div \square$ | **3** | $\square \div 9$
             $30 \div \square$

(b) $28 \div \square$
    $32 \div \square$ | **4** | $\square \div 6$
             $\square \div 9$

(c) $35 \div \square$
    $49 \div \square$ | **7** | $\square \div 8$
             $\square \div 6$

(d) $18 \div \square$
    $48 \div \square$ | **6** | $42 \div \square$
             $\square \div 9$

(e) $36 \div \square$
    $54 \div \square$ | **9** | $\square \div 8$
             $\square \div 9$

(f) $40 \div \square$
    $\square \div 3$ | **8** | $\square \div 4$
             $56 \div \square$

3.3 Remainders in division

14 pupils want to split into teams of 4.

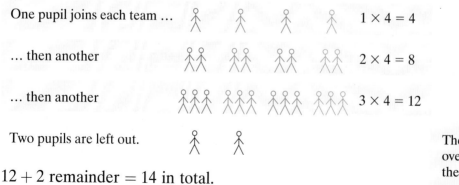

One pupil joins each team ... $1 \times 4 = 4$

... then another $2 \times 4 = 8$

... then another $3 \times 4 = 12$

Two pupils are left out.

The ones left
over are called
the **remainder**

$12 + 2$ remainder $= 14$ in total.

You write $14 \div 4 = 3$ remainder 2 —————————— Four teams of 3
You say: '14 divided by 4 is 3 remainder 2'.   with 2 left over

Example 3

Work out 41 ÷ 9

Look at the 9 times multiplication table.

36 is the biggest number which is less than 41

4 × 9 = 36 so 41 ÷ 9 = 4 remainder something.

41 − 36 = 5 so 41 ÷ 9 = 4 remainder 5.

$1 \times 9 = 9$
$2 \times 9 = 18$
$3 \times 9 = 27$
$4 \times 9 = 36$
$5 \times 9 = 45$

Exercise 3C

Work out:

1 **(a)** 17 ÷ 2   **(b)** 19 ÷ 3   **(c)** 29 ÷ 3
   (d) 23 ÷ 4   **(e)** 37 ÷ 4   **(f)** 49 ÷ 5
   (g) 37 ÷ 5   **(h)** 32 ÷ 3   **(i)** 43 ÷ 4
   (j) 44 ÷ 5   **(k)** 39 ÷ 4   **(l)** 31 ÷ 3

2 **(a)** 20 ÷ 6   **(b)** 36 ÷ 7   **(c)** 57 ÷ 8
   (d) 84 ÷ 9   **(e)** 49 ÷ 8   **(f)** 38 ÷ 8
   (g) 52 ÷ 6   **(h)** 43 ÷ 7   **(i)** 61 ÷ 8
   (j) 76 ÷ 9   **(k)** 34 ÷ 9   **(l)** 64 ÷ 7

3 Find the number halfway between:

   (a) 24 and 48   **(b)** 37 and 51   **(c)** 56 and 22
   (d) 54 and 38   **(e)** 26 and 34   **(f)** 47 and 27
   (g) 57 and 25   **(h)** 34 and 64   **(i)** 36 and 84

To find the number halfway between two others, add the two numbers together and divide by 2. Remember to divide the remainder by 2.

$1 \div 2 = \frac{1}{2}$

4 Find the number halfway between:

   (a) 35 and 48   **(b)** 36 and 57   **(c)** 17 and 46
   (d) 54 and 13   **(e)** 17 and 28   **(f)** 32 and 45
   (g) 63 and 12   **(h)** 18 and 35   **(i)** 27 and 62

3.4 Multiplication and division up to 10 × 10

Example 4

Mungo has to put 36 roses into bunches of 5. How many bunches can he make?

36 ÷ 5 = 7 remainder 1

He can make 7 bunches and has 1 rose left over.

Example 5

Val bought six books in a charity shop for £2 each.
How much did she pay in total?

Write your answer out like this:

Total cost = 6 × £2
            = £12

Example 6

Amber is arranging taxis to take 34 people
to a night-club. Each taxi takes 4 people.
How many taxis should she order?

34 ÷ 4 = 8 remainder 2

8 taxis will not be enough.
She should order 9.

Exercise 3D

1   Jeremiah runs 8 miles every day.
    How many miles does he run each week?

2   Mrs Cliss wants to buy a doughnut for each child in her
    class.
    There are 33 children in her class and the doughnuts
    are in packs of 6.
    How many packs must she buy?

3   A farmer is putting peaches into packets of 7.
    He has 50 peaches. How many packets can he fill?

4   Sixty people go to a restaurant
    for a Christmas dinner.
    How many tables will they
    need if each table seats
    eight people?

5   Every day Ruchi does the following exercises:
        8 sit-ups,   9 star jumps,   6 press-ups,   7 stretches
    How many of each exercise does she do in a week?

6 Thomas bought five packets of films.
Each packet contained four rolls of film and cost £9.

(a) How many rolls of film did he buy?
(b) What was the total cost of the films?

7 At a barn dance sixty people want to take part in the
first dance.
They must be in groups of eight for the dance.
Will all of the sixty people be able to take part in the
first dance?

3.5 Multiples

■ **The multiples of 5 are the answers in the 5 times
multiplication table.**

$1 \times 5 =$ **5**
$2 \times 5 =$ **10**
$3 \times 5 =$ **15**
. . .
. . .
. . .
$11 \times 5 =$ **55**
. . .
. . .
. . .

These numbers are the
multiples of 5.

$11 \times 5 = 55$
so 55 is a multiple
of 5.

1	2	3	4	**5**
6	7	8	9	**10**
11	12	13	14	**15** |...

If you write out the
counting numbers in
rows of 5, the numbers
in the last column are
the multiples of 5.

■ **The multiples of 2 are called EVEN numbers:**
2, 4, 6, 8, 10, 12, 14 ...
The units digit of an even number is always 0, 2, 4, 6, or 8.

■ **The other whole numbers are called ODD numbers:**
1, 3, 5, 7, 9, 11, 13, 15 ...
The units digit of an odd number is always 1, 3, 5, 7, or 9.

Example 7

Which multiples of 8 are between 30 and 50?
Think of the 8 times multiplication table.
The multiples of 8 between 30 and 50 are 32, 40 and 48.

$1 \times 8 = 8$
$2 \times 8 = 16$
$3 \times 8 = 24$
$4 \times 8 = 32$
$5 \times 8 = 40$
$6 \times 8 = 48$
$7 \times 8 = 56$

Exercise 3E

1 Write down the first ten even numbers.

2 Write down all the even numbers between 21 and 31.

3 What is the next even number after
(a) 53 (b) 47 (c) 95 (d) 153 (e) 89 (f) 28

4 Write down all the odd numbers between 30 and 40.

5 What is the next odd number after
(a) 34 (b) 46 (c) 92 (d) 132 (e) 39 (f) 57

6 Write down the first five multiples of 8.

7 Write down the first five multiples of 9.

8 Which multiples of 7 are between 40 and 60?

9 Which multiples of 6 are between 20 and 50?

> Remember:
> EVEN numbers end
> in 0, 2, 4, 6, or 8
> ODD numbers end
> in 1, 3, 5, 7, or 9

10 These numbers are multiples of four:
120, 124, 128, 132
What are the next two multiples of four?

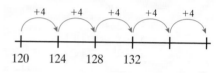
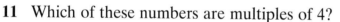

120 124 128 132

11 Which of these numbers are multiples of 4?
(a) 20 (b) 12 (c) 15
(d) 18 (e) 28 (f) 32

12 Which of these numbers are multiples of 6?
(a) 48 (b) 36 (c) 40
(d) 28 (e) 18 (f) 54

13 Draw a grid like this:
(a) Place the numbers from 1 to 9 in the grid so that each horizontal, vertical and diagonal line of three numbers adds up to an odd number.
(It does not have to be the same odd number for each line)
(b) Try and find other ways to arrange the numbers that work.
(c) Can each line add up to an even number?

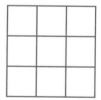

14 Copy and complete this table by writing odd or even.

+	odd	even
odd		
even		

If you add an odd number to an even number is the answer odd or even ?

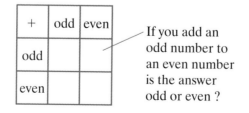

15 This line of counters is set out in a pattern. What colour is the

Hint:
Think about the
multiples of 8.

  (a) 24th counter
  (b) 66th counter

○ ○ ○ ○ ○ ● ● ● ○ ○ ○ ○ ○ ● ● ●

3.6 Factors

■ **The factors of a number are the numbers that divide into it exactly leaving no remainder.**

1, 2, 4 and 8 are the factors of 8. You can think of this as meaning:

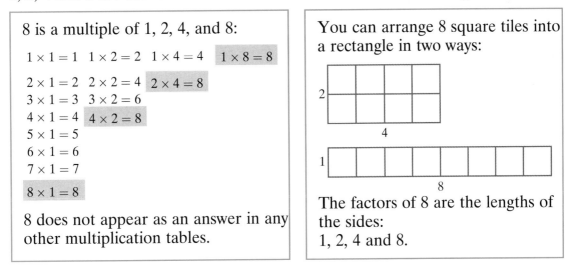

8 is a multiple of 1, 2, 4, and 8:

$1 \times 1 = 1$ $1 \times 2 = 2$ $1 \times 4 = 4$ $1 \times 8 = 8$

$2 \times 1 = 2$ $2 \times 2 = 4$ $2 \times 4 = 8$
$3 \times 1 = 3$ $3 \times 2 = 6$
$4 \times 1 = 4$ $4 \times 2 = 8$
$5 \times 1 = 5$
$6 \times 1 = 6$
$7 \times 1 = 7$
$8 \times 1 = 8$

8 does not appear as an answer in any other multiplication tables.

You can arrange 8 square tiles into a rectangle in two ways:

The factors of 8 are the lengths of the sides:
1, 2, 4 and 8.

Example 8

What are the factors of 6?
Find ways to arrange 6 square tiles into a rectangle.

The factors of 6 are the lengths of the sides: 1, 2, 3 and 6.

2×3

1×6

Example 9

Is 3 a factor of 18?

Write down the multiples of 3:

  3, 6, 9, 12, 15, 18, 21, …

18 is a multiple of 3, so 3 is a factor of 18.

Example 10

Which factor of 24
is missing from the cloud?

Put the factors into pairs:

$1 \times 24 = 24$
$2 \times 12 = 24$
$3 \times 8 \; = 24$
$4 \times 6 \; = 24$

4 is the missing factor.

Factors of 24

Exercise 3F

1   Use square tiles or squared paper for this question.
What are the factors of:

(a) 9	**(b)** 12	**(c)** 10	**(d)** 16	
(e) 18	**(f)** 21	**(g)** 28	**(h)** 30	
(i) 40	**(j)** 36	**(k)** 50	**(l)** 100	

Hint:
Factors are always
whole numbers.

2   True or false:

(a) 6 is a factor of 18   **(b)** 4 is a factor of 16
(c) 5 is a factor of 23   **(d)** 8 is a factor of 24
(e) 9 is a factor of 29   **(f)** 7 is a factor of 35
(g) 5 is a factor of 30   **(h)** 9 is a factor of 36
(i) 8 is a factor of 32   **(j)** 6 is a factor of 40

3   Which numbers have both these factors?

(a) 2 and 3   **(b)** 2 and 4
(c) 2 and 5   **(d)** 2 and 6
(e) What do you notice about your answers to
parts **a**, **b**, **c** and **d**?

4   Which numbers have both these factors?

(a) 3 and 4   **(b)** 3 and 5
(c) 3 and 6   **(d)** 3 and 7
(e) What do you notice about your answers to
parts **a**, **b**, **c** and **d**?

5   Find the missing factor by putting the numbers in the
cloud into factor pairs.

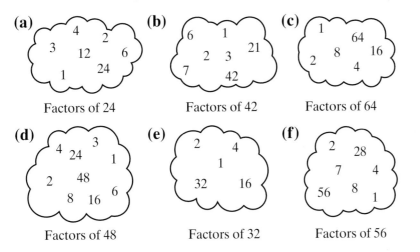

(a)
Factors of 24

(b)
Factors of 42

(c)
Factors of 64

Hint:
64 is a square
number so 8
pairs with
itself.

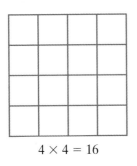

(d)
Factors of 48

(e)
Factors of 32

(f)
Factors of 56

3.7 Square numbers and square roots

You can arrange 16 square tiles into a square:

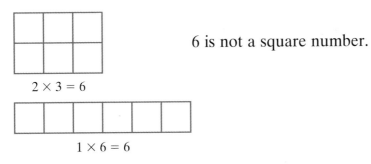

$4 \times 4 = 16$

16 is a square number.

You cannot arrange 6 square tiles into a square:

$2 \times 3 = 6$

6 is not a square number.

$1 \times 6 = 6$

■   **When you multiply a whole number by itself you get a
square number:**
$1 \times 1 = 1$, $2 \times 2 = 4$, $3 \times 3 = 9$, $4 \times 4 = 16$ ...
1, 4, 9, 16, 25 ... are square numbers.

■ **Every square number has a square root:**
1 is the square root of 1 because 1 × 1 = 1
2 is the square root of 4 because 2 × 2 = 4
3 is the square root of 9 because 3 × 3 = 9

You write:
$\sqrt{1} = 1$
$\sqrt{4} = 2$
$\sqrt{9} = 3$

Exercise 3G

1   Write down the first twenty square numbers.

2   What is the square root of:

(a) 25   (b) 49   (c) 64   (d) 81
(e) 100   (f) 36   (g) 121   (h) 169
(i) 225   (j) 256   (k) 324   (l) 400

3   Activity

(a) How many cubes do you need to build each of the double sided staircases shown?

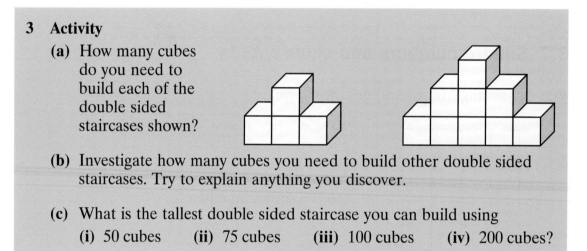

(b) Investigate how many cubes you need to build other double sided staircases. Try to explain anything you discover.

(c) What is the tallest double sided staircase you can build using
    (i) 50 cubes   (ii) 75 cubes   (iii) 100 cubes   (iv) 200 cubes?

4   To draw the factor star of a number write it in a circle and add a point for each of its factors.
(a) Investigate factor stars for the numbers up to 20.
(b) When does a factor star have an odd number of points?
Explain your answer.

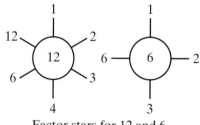

Factor stars for 12 and 6.

3.8 Multiplying 2- and 3-digit numbers by a 1-digit number

You can do calculations like 29 × 4 by splitting them into two easy multiplications.
You need to be able to do calculations such as 20 × 4:

You know that $2 \times 4 = 8$.

Think of this with 1 p coins:

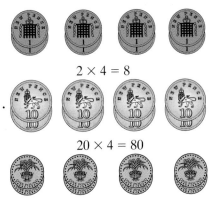

$2 \times 4 = 8$

Replace each 1 p with a 10 p ...

$20 \times 4 = 80$

... or a £1.00 coin:

$200 \times 4 = 800$

Remember:
£2.00 = 200 p
£8.00 = 800 p

$2 \times 4 = 8$ so $20 \times 4 = 80$ and $200 \times 4 = 800$.

Exercise 3H

Work out:

1 (a) 30×2 (b) 30×4 (c) 40×3 (d) 30×5
   (e) 40×6 (f) 20×9 (g) 50×7 (h) 20×6
   (i) 70×4 (j) 60×4 (k) 80×3 (l) 90×6

2 (a) 400×2 (b) 600×3 (c) 500×7 (d) 300×4
   (e) 700×4 (f) 200×5 (g) 600×7 (h) 900×7
   (i) 800×7 (j) 500×5 (k) 800×4 (l) 600×8

3 (a) 70×5 (b) 400×8 (c) 60×6 (d) 900×8
   (e) 300×8 (f) 600×9 (g) 80×6 (h) 70×6
   (i) 300×9 (j) 900×9 (k) 40×7 (l) 700×9

Example 11

Find an approximate answer to 74×6

   Round 74 to the nearest 10:   70
   Multiply 70 by 6 $70 \times 6 = 420$
   So $74 \times 6 \approx 420$

Remember:
$\approx$ means
'approximately
equal to'.

Example 12

Find an approximate answer to 383×7

   Round 383 to the nearest hundred: 400
   Multiply 400 by 7 $400 \times 7 = 2800$
   So $383 \times 7 \approx 2800$

There is more
on rounding
on p. 15.

Example 13

(a) Work out 29×4.

Think of 29 as $20 + 9$.

You know that $\quad 20 \times 4 = 80$
and $\quad\quad\quad\quad\quad 9 \times 4 = 36$
add the answers: $\quad 29 \times 4 = 116$

(b) Work out 640×3

Think of 640 as $600 + 40$

You know that $\quad 600 \times 3 = 1800$
and $\quad\quad\quad\quad\quad 40 \times 3 = 120$
add the answers: $\quad 640 \times 3 = 1920$

For harder multiplications you can set out your working like this:

Example 14

Work out 397×6.

First estimate the answer:

397 rounds to 400 so:

$$397 \times 6 \approx 400 \times 6$$
$$= 2400$$

so the answer should be approximately 2400.

Now calculate the answer accurately:

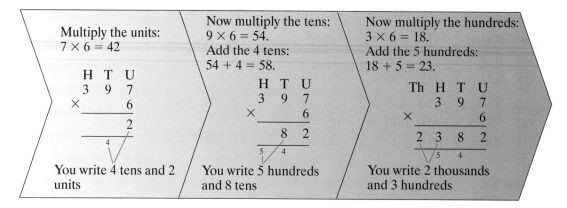

Multiply the units:
$7 \times 6 = 42$

H	T	U
3	9	7
×		6
		2

You write 4 tens and 2 units

Now multiply the tens:
$9 \times 6 = 54$.
Add the 4 tens:
$54 + 4 = 58$.

H	T	U
3	9	7
×		6
	8	2

You write 5 hundreds and 8 tens

Now multiply the hundreds:
$3 \times 6 = 18$.
Add the 5 hundreds:
$18 + 5 = 23$.

Th	H	T	U
	3	9	7
×			6
2	3	8	2

You write 2 thousands and 3 hundreds

So $397 \times 6 = 2382$.

This is very close to the estimated answer of 2400.

Example 15

A school ordered 8 boxes of 144 pencils.
How many pencils did the school order?

$144 \times 8 = 1152$ pencils.

```
    1 4 4
  ×     8
  1 1 5 2
    3 3
```

Always remember to add in the 'carry' numbers.

Exercise 3I

Find the approximate answers to:

1   (a) 54×6 (b) 27×8 (c) 46×7 (d) 83×6
      (e) 75×4 (f) 97×3 (g) 62×9 (h) 85×7

2   (a) 281×2 (b) 364×4 (c) 827×8 (d) 652×3
      (e) 791×9 (f) 803×7 (g) 981×6 (h) 947×5

3   Work out: Use the method in
      (a) 35×5 (b) 27×9 (c) 63×8 example 13.
      (d) 96×3 (e) 51×7 (f) 42×4
      (g) 77×6 (h) 38×7 (i) 270×4
      (j) 750×2 (k) 450×9 (l) 620×3

4   Work out:
      (a) 237×3 (b) 448×2 (c) 124×4 (d) 258×3
      (e) 496×2 (f) 274×3 (g) 473×5 (h) 347×4
      (i) 649×4 (j) 379×5 (k) 859×4 (l) 873×5

5   Work out:
      (a) 476×6 (b) 568×8 (c) 894×6 (d) 523×9
      (e) 832×7 (f) 586×8 (g) 743×9 (h) 219×7
      (i) 573×8 (j) 354×7 (k) 389×9 (l) 879×6

6   Beth delivers 164 newspapers
daily from Monday to Saturday.
How many newspapers does
she deliver in a week?

7   Mr Hewitt travels by train to work 5 days a week.
The return journey is 137 miles.
How many miles does he travel each week?

8   A machine makes 987 glass bottles an hour.
How many bottles can the machine make in 8 hours?

9   The cost of a flight to New York is £354.
How much would it cost for eight basketball players
and their manager to fly to New York?

3.9 Multiplying a 3-digit number by a 2-digit number

This section shows you how to do multiplications such as
473×64

Think of 64 as $60 + 4$

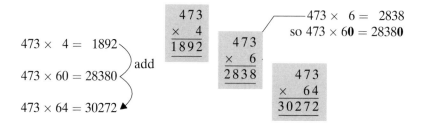

$473 \times 4 = 1892$
$473 \times 60 = 28380$ } add
$473 \times 64 = 30272$

$$
\begin{array}{r}
4\ 7\ 3 \\
\times\ \ \ 4 \\
\hline
1892
\end{array}
$$

$$
\begin{array}{r}
4\ 7\ 3 \\
\times\ \ \ 6 \\
\hline
2838
\end{array}
$$

$473 \times 6 = 2838$
so $473 \times 60 = 28380$

$$
\begin{array}{r}
4\ 7\ 3 \\
\times\ \ 6\ 4 \\
\hline
30272
\end{array}
$$

You can set out 473×64 like this:

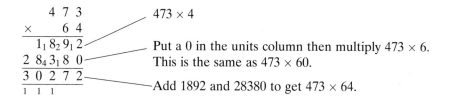

$$
\begin{array}{r}
4\ 7\ 3 \\
\times\ \ \ \ 6\ 4 \\
\hline
1_18_29_12 \\
2\ 8_43_18\ 0 \\
\hline
3\ 0\ 2\ 7\ 2 \\
\hline
{\scriptstyle 1\ \ 1\ \ 1}
\end{array}
$$

473×4

Put a 0 in the units column then multiply 473×6.
This is the same as 473×60.

Add 1892 and 28380 to get 473×64.

Exercise 3J

1 (a) 212×21 (b) 123×23
    (c) 234×32 (d) 595×81
    (e) 217×95 (f) 783×23
    (g) 236×57 (h) 142×53
    (i) 810×42 (j) 162×35
    (k) 678×52 (l) 909×64

2 Choose any five digits, for example 2, 3, 6, 8, 9. Write
them as a 3-digit $\times$ 2-digit multiplication and work out
the answer.
Try other arrangements of your five digits. Which
arrangement gives the largest answer?
Which arrangement gives the smallest answer?

$$
\begin{array}{r}
6\ 2\ 8 \\
\times\ \ \ 3\ 9 \\
\hline
5\ 6_25_72 \\
1\ 8\ 8_24\ 0 \\
\hline
2\ 4\ 4\ 9\ 2 \\
\hline
{\scriptstyle 1\ \ 1}
\end{array}
$$

3.10 Dividing a 3-digit number by a 1-digit number

To do large divisions you can set your work out like this:

Find $586 \div 3$.

Divide 5 hundreds by 3: $5 \div 3 = 1$ remainder 2. $\dfrac{1}{3\overline{)5\,^2 8\,6}}$ Add 2 hundreds to 8 tens to make 28 tens.	Divide 28 tens by 3: $28 \div 3 = 9$ remainder 1. $\dfrac{1\ 9}{3\overline{)5\,^2 8\,^1 6}}$ Add 1 ten to 6 units to make 16 units.	Divide 16 units by 3: $16 \div 3 = 5$ remainder 1. $\dfrac{1\ 9\ 5}{3\overline{)5\,^2 8\,^1 6}}$ rem 1.

So $586 \div 3 = 195$ remainder 1.

Example 16

A fruit grower packs 765 peaches in packs of 6.
How many packs can she fill?

$765 \div 6 = 127$ remainder 3 ————————

$$\dfrac{1\ 2\ 7}{6\overline{)7\,^1 6\,^4 5}}\ \text{remainder } 3$$

She can fill 127 packs with 3 peaches left over.

Example 17

Seven people share a lottery win of £952.
How much do they get each?

$952 \div 7 = 136$ ————————————

$$\dfrac{1\ 3\ 6}{7\overline{)9\,^2 5\,^4 2}}$$

They each get £136.

Exercise 3K

1 Work out:

   (a) $837 \div 3$ (b) $548 \div 2$ (c) $924 \div 4$
   (d) $958 \div 3$ (e) $365 \div 2$ (f) $574 \div 3$
   (g) $437 \div 5$ (h) $374 \div 4$ (i) $695 \div 4$
   (j) $796 \div 5$ (k) $853 \div 4$ (l) $763 \div 5$

2 Work out:

(a) $786 \div 6$ (b) $548 \div 2$ (c) $834 \div 6$
(d) $537 \div 9$ (e) $259 \div 7$ (f) $386 \div 8$
(g) $973 \div 9$ (h) $819 \div 7$ (i) $273 \div 8$
(j) $398 \div 7$ (k) $489 \div 9$ (l) $949 \div 6$

3 Five friends share 113 sweets equally between them.
How many will each friend get?
How many will be left over?

4 Three friends each drive an equal amount of a 411 mile trip.
How far do they each drive?

5 A gardener plants 638 flowers in rows of 7.
How many rows can she plant?

6 A farmer gives an equal number of seeds to each of her 9 workers and plants the remainder herself.
How many will she have to plant if she starts with:

(a) 286 seeds   (b) 735 seeds   (c) 693 seeds   (d) 8 seeds?

3.11 Dividing a 3-digit number by a 2-digit number

This section shows you how to do divisions such as $875 \div 24$.

First, here is a simpler example: $947 \div 4$

Divide the 9 hundreds by 4
$9 \div 4 = 2$ remainder 1

$$\begin{array}{r} 2 \\ 4\overline{)9\,^{1}4\,7} \end{array}$$

Divide the 14 tens by 4
$14 \div 4 = 3$ remainder 2

$$\begin{array}{r} 2\;3 \\ 4\overline{)9\,^{1}4\,^{2}7} \end{array}$$

Divide the 27 units by 4
$27 \div 4 = 6$ remainder 3

$$\begin{array}{r} 2\;3\;6\text{ rem. }3 \\ 4\overline{)9\,^{1}4\,^{2}7} \end{array}$$

You could also set it out like this:

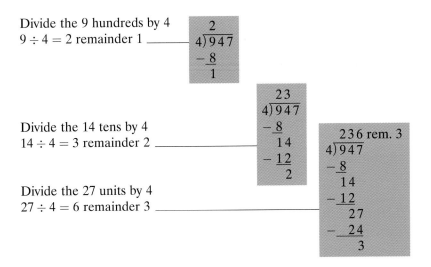

Divide the 9 hundreds by 4
9 ÷ 4 = 2 remainder 1

Divide the 14 tens by 4
14 ÷ 4 = 3 remainder 2

Divide the 27 units by 4
27 ÷ 4 = 6 remainder 3

The second method looks complicated but it is a good way
to set out a division such as 875 ÷ 24.

You can set out 875 ÷ 24 like this:

You cannot divide the 8 hundreds by 24.
Divide the 87 tens by 24.
87 ÷ 24 = 3 remainder 15

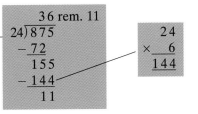

Divide the 155 units by 24.
155 ÷ 24 = 6 remainder 11

Exercise 3L

1 **(a)** 376 ÷ 15   **(b)** 805 ÷ 12   **(c)** 707 ÷ 18
    (d) 215 ÷ 17   **(e)** 164 ÷ 19   **(f)** 990 ÷ 14

2 **(a)** 147 ÷ 25   **(b)** 432 ÷ 33   **(c)** 438 ÷ 29
    (d) 231 ÷ 47   **(e)** 329 ÷ 41   **(f)** 650 ÷ 36

3 **(a)** 506 ÷ 55   **(b)** 695 ÷ 67   **(c)** 941 ÷ 58
    (d) 281 ÷ 96   **(e)** 812 ÷ 89   **(f)** 723 ÷ 70

Exercise 3M

You must decide whether to use multiplication or division for each question.

1 Ray's gym ordered 8 packs of cola.
  Each pack contained 48 cans.
  How many cans of cola did they order?

2 A farmer packs 872 eggs into boxes of 6.
  How many boxes can she fill?

3 A decorator charges £18 per hour. He charges Mrs
  Khan £81 to paint the front room. How many hours of
  decorating was she charged for?

4 A school ordered 315 books at £12 each. What was the
  total cost of the books?

5 A shop bought seven display cabinets at £645 each.
  What was the total cost of the cabinets?

6 A school canteen prepares 476 meals each day.
  How many meals are prepared in a normal school
  week?

7 A racing cyclist wants to do at least 800 miles of
  training a week.
  He wants to do the same number of miles each day.
  How many miles should he cycle each day?

8 Sixteen people share the cost of hiring a hall for a
  party. The hall cost £1200 to hire.
  How much did each person have to pay?

9 Ambrose is planning a party.
  He wants to give everyone a glass of champagne
  for a toast.
  He has invited 152 people and each bottle of
  champagne will fill six glasses.
  How many bottles of champagne must he buy?

10 A shop ordered seven video recorders at £387 each.
   What was the total cost of the video recorders?

11 Each Saturday Jonathan expects to sell 500 hot dogs on his stall. Sausages come in packs of 6 and bread rolls come in packs of 8.
   (a) How many packs of sausages must he buy?
   (b) How many packs of bread rolls must he buy?

12 A man travels from Cardiff to Builth Wells and back every day for three days.
If he travels a total of 456 miles, how far is it from Cardiff to Builth Wells?

13 Eight people each paid £237 to hire a boat for a holiday.
How much did the boat cost to hire?

Summary of key points

1 Division is the opposite of multiplication.
For example $3 \times 6 = 18$ so $18 \div 6 = 3$
                                and $18 \div 3 = 6$

2 The multiples of 5 are the answers in the 5 times multiplication table
   5, 10, 15, 20, 25 . . .

3 The multiples of 2 are called EVEN numbers:
   2, 4, 6, 8, 10, 12, 14 . . .
Even numbers always end with 0, 2, 4, 6, or 8.

The other whole numbers are called ODD numbers:
   1, 3, 5, 7, 9, 11, 13, 15 . . .
Odd numbers always end with 1, 3, 5, 7, or 9.

4 The factors of a number are the numbers that divide into it exactly leaving no remainder.

5 When you multiply a whole number by itself you get a square number.
$1 \times 1 = 1$, $2 \times 2 = 4$, $3 \times 3 = 9$, $4 \times 4 = 16 \ldots$
1, 4, 9, 16, 25 ... are square numbers.

6 Every square number has a square root:
1 is the square root of 1 because $1 \times 1 = 1$
2 is the square root of 4 because $2 \times 2 = 4$
3 is the square root of 9 because $3 \times 3 = 9$

4 Working with algebra

Algebra is a branch of
mathematics that uses
letters to represent numbers.

Scientists use complicated algebra to work
out the paths of rockets.

4.1 Using letters to represent numbers

In algebra you can use a letter to represent a number you
do not yet know.

Example 1

Jessica has a box of books.
You don't know how many books she has.
Using algebra you could say:

Jessica has *b* books.

She buys 5 more ...

... now she has *b* + 5 books.

Example 2

Mark has d tennis balls and Jane has e tennis balls.
How many tennis balls do they have altogether?

Altogether they have $d + e$ tennis balls.

Example 3

Ben has y coins in his collection.
He gives 5 coins to Julian.
How many coins does he have left?

Ben had y coins.
Now he has y coins minus 5 coins.
So Ben has $y - 5$ coins.

Exercise 4A

1 Shami has some pens – but you don't know how many.
   Use algebra to say how many pens he has.

2 **(a)** Ingrid doesn't know how many books she has
      Use algebra to say how many books she has.
   (b) She buys 7 new books.
      How many books does she have altogether?

3 Vicky has m shrubs. She plants 14 more.
   How many shrubs does Vicky have now?

4 Neil has x mugs and Cathy has y mugs.
   How many mugs do they have altogether?

5 Megan has a pens and Harvey has b pens.
   How many pens do they have altogether?

6 Paula has 12 apples. Vijay has d apples.
   How many apples do they have altogether?

7 Margaret has r posters and she gives t of them to Karen.
   How many posters does Margaret have left?

8 d spectators are watching a cricket match. 20 of them
   leave after lunch.
   Use algebra to say how many spectators are left after
   lunch.

9 Write your own questions that have these answers:
   (a) $p + 2$ **(b)** $c - 10$ **(c)** $e + 3$ **(d)** $12 + d$ **(e)** $3 + a$
   (f) $x - z$ **(g)** $a + n$ **(h)** $b + a + 2$ **(i)** $c - f + 6$

4.2 Collecting letters

At a school fête the stalls give out
tokens for prizes. Each colour token
is worth a different number of points:

A red token is worth *r* points:

A blue token is worth *b* points:

A green token is worth *g* points:

Knock over all the cans to get 2 blue tokens

Example 4

Halfway through the fête Shiraz has these tokens:

How many points does he have?

3 blue tokens	4 green tokens	1 red token

$b + b + b$
3*b* points

$g + g + g + g$
4*g* points

r
r points

Altogether he has $3b$ + $4g$ + r points.

1 lot of *r*.
You write *r* **not** 1*r*.

■   **In algebra you write 1 lot of *r* as *r*. You don't write 1*r*.**

Example 5

Collect letters to write these in a shorter form:

(a) $a + a + a + a$

(b) $d + d + d + d + d + d$

(a) $a + a + a + a = 4$ lots of *a*
     $= 4a$

(b) $d + d + d + d + d + d = 6$ lots of *d*
     $= 6d$

Example 6

Write in a longer form:

(a) $3x$

(b) $6y$

(a) $3x = 3$ lots of *x*
     $= x + x + x$

(b) $6y = 6$ lots of *y*
     $= y + y + y + y + y + y$

Exercise 4B

Write these in a shorter form:

1 $a + a$ **2** $b + b$

3 $x + x$ **4** $w + w + w$

5 $y + y + y + y$ **6** $a + a + a + a + a$

7 $b + b + b$ **8** $x + x + x + x$

9 $w + w + w + w + w + w + w$ **10** $t + t + t + t + t + t + t$

11 $r + r + r + r + r$ **12** $x + x + x + x + x + x + x + x$

13 $a + a + a + a$ **14** $y + y + y + y + y + y + y$

15 $x + x + x$ **16** $t + t + t + t + t$

17 $r + r + r + r + r + r$ **18** $c + c + c$

19 $d + d + d$ **20** $e + e + e + e + e + e$

Write these in a longer form:

21 $3g$ **22** $4t$ **23** $2w$ **24** $7r$

25 $5y$ **26** $8w$ **27** $5x$ **28** $3a$

29 $5w$ **30** $5r$ **31** $6a$ **32** $4s$

33 Write down the length of each line as simply as possible:

(a)

x	x	x	x

(b)

y	y	y	y	y	y	y	y	y

4.3 Collecting like terms

Shiraz had $3b + 4g + r$ points halfway through the fête.

■ 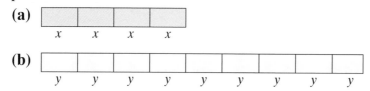 $3b + 4g + r$ is an *algebraic expression*

Each part is called a term.

Terms that use the same letter are called **like terms**.

You can often make an algebraic expression simpler by collecting like terms together.

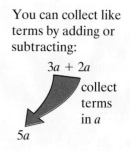

You can collect like terms by adding or subtracting:

$3a + 2a$

collect terms in a

$5a$

Example 7

Simplify if possible:

(a) $3b + 4b$ **(b)** $5x - 2x$ **(c)** $5c + 2d$ **(d)** $11g - g$

(a) $3b$ and $4b$ are both terms in b.

3 lots of b	$+$	4 lots of b	$=$	7 lots of b
so $3b$	$+$	$4b$	$=$	$7b$

> The term $3b$ uses the letter b. It is also called a **term in *b*.**

(b) $5x$ and $2x$ are both terms in x.

5 lots of x	$+$	2 lots of x	$=$	7 lots of x
so $5x$	$+$	$2x$	$=$	$7x$

(c) $5c$ and $2d$ use different letters.

  $5c$ $+$ $2d$ cannot be simplified.

(d) $11g$ and g are both terms in g.

11 lots of g	$+$	1 lot of g	$=$	12 lots of g.
so $11g$	$+$	g	$=$	$12g$

Exercise 4C

1 Simplify these expressions by collecting like terms:

(a) $3a + 3a$ **(b)** $4a - 3a$ **(c)** $4b + 3b$
(d) $7b - 4b$ **(e)** $b + 8b$ **(f)** $3a + 4a$
(g) $8x + 3x$ **(h)** $9r - 7r$ **(i)** $3x - x$
(j) $3y + 4y$ **(k)** $3y + 3y$ **(l)** $3a + 3a + 4a$
(m) $4b + 7b + 3b$ **(n)** $4p + 8p + p$ **(o)** $21x + 10x + 17x$
(p) $8a - 7a + 4a$ **(q)** $3x + 4x + 5x$ **(r)** $9a + 5a - 7a$
(s) $11x + 4x - 7x$ **(t)** $a + 2a + 3a$ **(u)** $15p - 10p - 5p$

2 Which expression has each pupil chosen from the board?

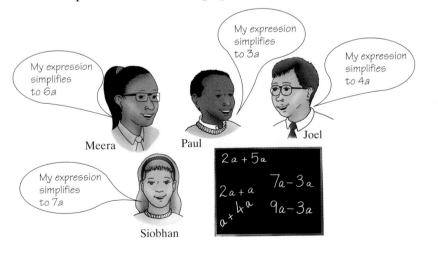

My expression simplifies to 6a

My expression simplifies to 3a

My expression simplifies to 4a

Meera   Paul   Joel

My expression simplifies to 7a

Siobhan

$2a + 5a$

$2a + a$

$a + 4a$

$7a - 3a$

$9a - 3a$

3   How many different expressions of your own can you find that are equal to $5b$?

4   Choose one term from each hexagon. How many different answers can you find?

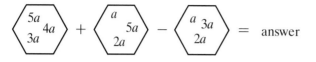

4.4 Simplifying expressions

Shiraz's friend Erica has 2 blue tokens, 2 green tokens and 5 red tokens. You can write Erica's points as an algebraic expression:

$2b + 2g + 5r$

Altogether Shiraz and Erica have:

Collect and then add all the like terms:

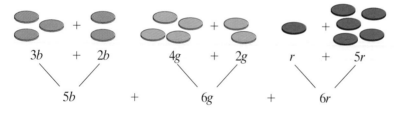

So they have $5b + 6g + 6r$ points altogether.

Example 8

Simplify $5x + 2y - 3x + 7y$

First collect like terms:

Next combine the terms:

$5x + 2y - 3x + 7y$

$5x - 3x + 2y + 7y$

$2x + 9y$

Remember: the sign is part of the term.
$5x + 2y - 3x + 7y$

the term is $-3x$

Example 9

Simplify $3a + 10 + 4a - 4$

First collect like terms:

Next combine the terms:

$3a + 10 + 4a - 4$

$3a + 4a + 10 - 4$

$7a + 6$

Exercise 4D

Simplify:

(a) $3a + 3b + 3a + 5b$

(b) $5c + 3d + 3c + 5d$

(c) $3r + 3s - 3r + 5s$

(d) $5x + 9y + 5x - 5y$

(e) $5w + 10s + 3w + 7s$

(f) $10a + 8b - 3a - 5b$

(g) $c + 5d + 5c - d$

(h) $3a + 10 + 7a + 8$

(i) $10b + 9 - 2b - 5$

(j) $3r + 10s - 5a - 9s$

(k) $7t + 3t - 5t + t$

(l) $10s - 5s - 3s - s$

(m) $3x + 7y + 7x - 5x$

(n) $5a + 8b + 3s - 3a + 3b$

(o) $8q + 3 + 5q - q + 3$

(p) $15p + 8d - 8p - 8d + 3$

(q) $5p + 5q - 5p + 5q$

(r) $10a + 3b + 5b + 10b + a$

(s) $8s + 7r - 5r - 3s$

(t) $5p + 5d + 5d + p + d$

(u) $8c + 3c + 3 + 5c - 3$

(v) $e + 8d + 3c - 7d + c$

(w) $15c + 10r - 5c - 5c + 3r$

(x) $15a + 8b + 5a - 10a + b - 3a$

(y) $5a + 5a - 3a + 7b - 3a + b$

(z) $15a + 5b + 3a - 5b + 3$

4.5 Multiplying in algebra

In algebra it is easy to confuse x with $\times$ so you usually leave out the multiplication sign.

Example 10

Write these expressions without multiplication signs:

(a) $\quad 3 \times a$

$\quad = 3a$

(b) $\quad x \times y$

$\quad = xy$

(c) $\quad \frac{1}{2} \times x$

$\quad = \frac{1}{2}x$

Example 11

Write $2 \times a \times 3 \times b$ in a shorter form.

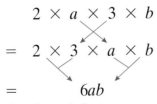

$$2 \times a \times 3 \times b$$

$$= 2 \times 3 \times a \times b$$

$$= \qquad 6ab$$

So $2 \times a \times 3 \times b = 6ab$

■ **Always write the numbers first then the letters in alphabetical order.**

Exercise 4E

1 Write these in a shorter form. The first one has been done for you.

 (a) $a \times b = ab$ **(b)** $c \times d$ **(c)** $3 \times a$

 (d) $2 \times p$ **(e)** $3 \times x \times y$ **(f)** $7 \times r \times s \times t$

 (g) $8 \times p \times q \times r$ **(h)** $e \times f \times g \times h$ **(i)** $5 \times a \times b \times c \times d \times e$

 (j) $10 \times r \times x \times s \times t$ **(k)** $3 \times a \times 2 \times b$ **(l)** $4 \times s \times t \times 3 \times v$

2 Write these in a longer form, using multiplication signs. The first one has been done for you.

 (a) $ps = p \times s$ **(b)** tr **(c)** $4y$

 (d) $7g$ **(e)** $2ab$ **(f)** $11abc$

 (g) $abcd$ **(h)** $2rstw$ **(i)** $3xyz$

4.6 Multiplying terms together

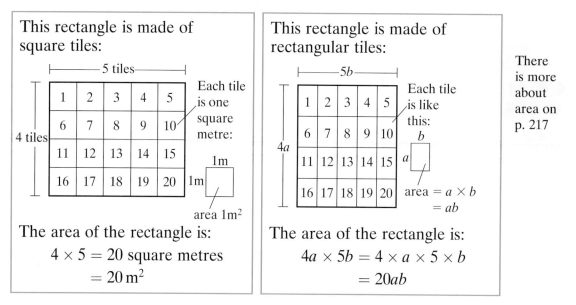

This rectangle is made of square tiles:

5 tiles — 4 tiles

Each tile is one square metre: 1m, 1m, area 1m²

The area of the rectangle is:

$$4 \times 5 = 20 \text{ square metres}$$
$$= 20 \text{ m}^2$$

This rectangle is made of rectangular tiles:

5b — 4a

Each tile is like this: b, a, area $= a \times b = ab$

The area of the rectangle is:

$$4a \times 5b = 4 \times a \times 5 \times b$$
$$= 20ab$$

There is more about area on p. 217

■ **To multiply 4a by 5b:**

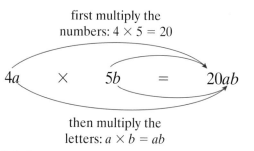

first multiply the numbers: $4 \times 5 = 20$

$$4a \quad \times \quad 5b \quad = \quad 20ab$$

then multiply the letters: $a \times b = ab$

Remember to write the numbers first, then the letters in alphabetical order

■ **To multiply terms together, first multiply the numbers, then multiply the letters.**

Example 12

Work out:

(a) $2a \times 3b$ **(b)** $2ab \times 3c$

(a) Multiply the numbers first:
$$2 \times 3 = 6$$
Then multiply the letters:
$$a \times b = ab$$
So $2a \times 3b = 6 \times ab$
$$= 6ab$$

(b) Multiply the numbers first:
$$2 \times 3 = 6$$
Then multiply the letters:
$$ab \times c = abc$$
So $2ab \times 3c = 6 \times abc$
$$= 6abc$$

Exercise 4F

1   Work out the area of each rectangle:

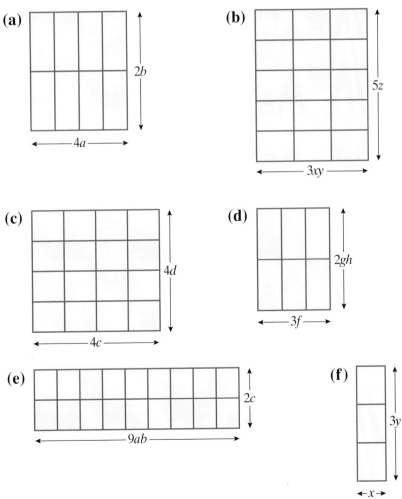

(a) $2b$, $4a$

(b) $5z$, $3xy$

(c) $4d$, $4c$

(d) $2gh$, $3f$

(e) $2c$, $9ab$

(f) $3y$, x

2   Multiply the following:

(a) $2a \times 5b$ (b) $3a \times 4b$ (c) $4a \times 5b$

(d) $3x \times 3y$ (e) $4x \times 2y$ (f) $3a \times 7b$

(g) $6c \times 3d$ (h) $c \times 2d$ (i) $4p \times 5r$ Hint: c means $1 \times c$

(j) $6r \times 5s$ (k) $7a \times 3b$ (l) $4x \times y$

(m) $2x \times 3y$ (n) $6a \times 5b$ (o) $2ab \times 4c$

(p) $3ab \times 2c$ (q) $4xy \times 3z$ (r) $5p \times 2st$

(s) $7cd \times 2e$ (t) $6ab \times 3c$ (u) $2ab \times 2cd$

(v) $3xy \times 4wz$ (w) $2mn \times 6pq$ (x) $9ab \times 3cde$

(y) $abc \times 7de$ (z) $4cd \times 3efg$

Summary of key points

1   In algebra you write 1 lot of r as r.
You don't write $1r$.

2    $3b + 4g + r$ is an *algebraic expression*.

Each part is called a term.

3   Always write the numbers first then the letters in alphabetical order.

4   To multiply terms together, first multiply the numbers, then multiply the letters.

5 Number patterns

Images like these are called fractals. You can generate them using number patterns on a computer.

5.1 Patterns from matchsticks and dots

Look at this matchstick pattern:

3 matches …   5 matches …   7 matches …   9 matches …

In numbers the pattern is:

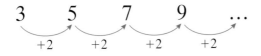

3   5   7   9   …

+2   +2   +2   +2

The rule to go from one shape to the next is **+2**.

Look at this dot pattern.

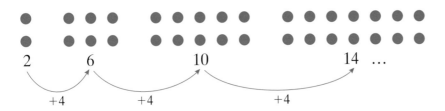

2   6   10   14 …

+4   +4   +4

The rule to go from one shape to the next is **+4**.

Exercise 5A

1 Copy these shape patterns.
For each one, draw the next two shapes.

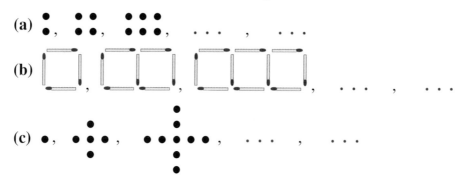

(a) •, •• , ••• , . . . , . . .
      • ••   •••

(b) ▢, ▢▢, ▢▢▢, . . . , . . .

(c) •, • , • • , . . . , . . .

2 For these shape patterns:
  • write down the number sequence, filling in the missing numbers;
  • write down the rule to go from one shape to the next.

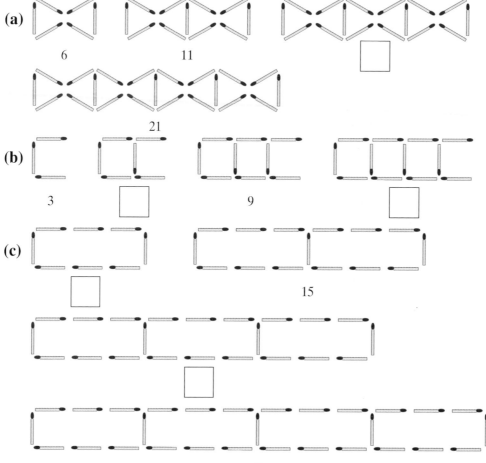

(a)

        6   11   ☐

                  21

(b)

    3   ☐   9   ☐

(c)

        ☐   15

              ☐

(d)

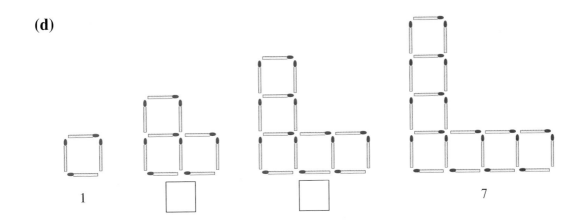

1   7

3 For these shape patterns:
- draw the next two shapes;
- write down the rule to go from one shape to the next.

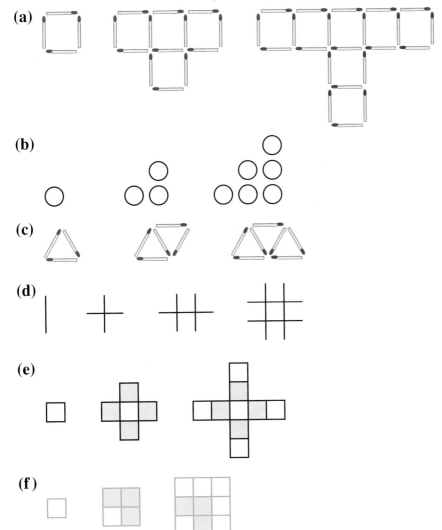

(a)

(b)

(c)

(d)

(e)

(f)

5.2 Number machines

■ **You can use number machines to make number patterns:**

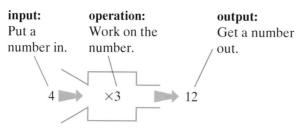

input:
Put a number in.

operation:
Work on the number.

output:
Get a number out.

This is a '×3' number machine. The **operation** is 'multiply by 3'.

Here is a two step number machine.
The output from the first machine becomes the input to the second machine.

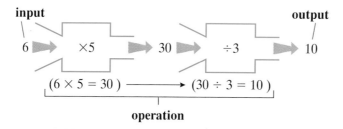

Remember: this machine is called a two step machine because there are two operations.

Write down the output numbers for these number machines:

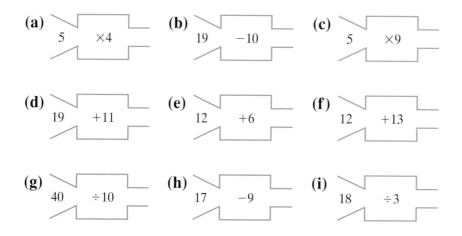

(a) 5 ×4

(b) 19 −10

(c) 5 ×9

(d) 19 +11

(e) 12 +6

(f) 12 +13

(g) 40 ÷10

(h) 17 −9

(i) 18 ÷3

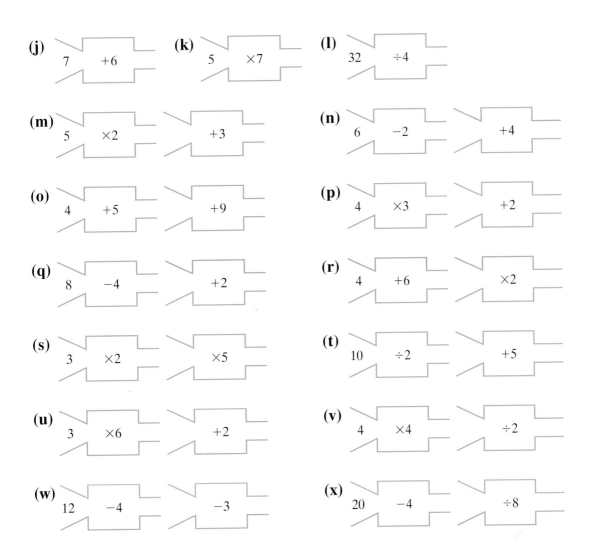

(j) 7 +6

(k) 5 ×7

(l) 32 ÷4

(m) 5 ×2 → +3

(n) 6 −2 → +4

(o) 4 +5 → +9

(p) 4 ×3 → +2

(q) 8 −4 → +2

(r) 4 +6 → ×2

(s) 3 ×2 → ×5

(t) 10 ÷2 → +5

(u) 3 ×6 → +2

(v) 4 ×4 → ÷2

(w) 12 −4 → −3

(x) 20 −4 → ÷8

Example 1

What is the output if you input the number pattern
1, 2, 3, 4 into a ×9 number machine?

input ▶ ×9 ▶ output

1	1 × 9 = 9	9
2	2 × 9 = 18	18
3	3 × 9 = 27	27
4	4 × 9 = 36	36

If you put a pattern
into a number
machine the output
numbers make a
pattern too:
input:
1, 2, 3, 4, ...
The rule is 'add
one'.
output:
9, 18, 27, 36, ...
The rule is 'add
nine'.

You can also show this in a table:

The input numbers go in this column

×9	
1	9
2	18
3	27
4	36

Write the operation in here

The output numbers go in this column

Exercise 5C

1 Copy and complete the tables:

(a)

×3	
1	3
2	
3	9
4	
5	

(b)

×5	
1	
2	
3	15
4	
5	

(c)

+8	
1	
2	
3	
4	12
5	

(d)

−1	
1	
2	
3	
4	
5	

(e)

×2	
2	
4	
6	
8	
10	

(f)

×10	
2	
4	
6	
8	
10	

(g)

+8	
1	
3	
5	
7	
9	

(h)

×5	
1	
3	
5	
7	
9	

(i)

×2	
10	
20	
30	
40	
50	

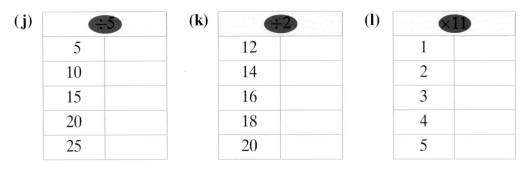

(j) ÷5	
5	
10	
15	
20	
25	

(k) ÷2	
12	
14	
16	
18	
20	

(l) ×11	
1	
2	
3	
4	
5	

2 Use input numbers 1, 2, 3, 4 and 5 to find the output numbers for the following operations. Show your work in tables.

(**a**) +7 (**b**) ×4 (**c**) +12 (**d**) ×6
(**e**) +20 (**f**) −1 (**g**) ÷2 (**h**) ×12

3 Use input numbers 12, 16, 20, 24 and 28 for the following operations. Show your answers in tables.

(**a**) +8 (**b**) ÷4 (**c**) −9 (**d**) ×2
(**e**) ×10 (**f**) ÷2 (**g**) −11 (**h**) +18

You can also show two step number machines in a table:

Example 2

What is the output from a +5 × 2 number machine if you input the number pattern 2, 4, 6, 8?

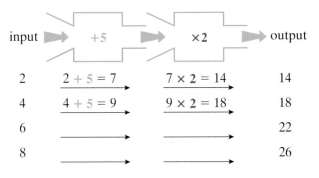

input	+5	×2	output
2	2 + 5 = 7	7 × 2 = 14	14
4	4 + 5 = 9	9 × 2 = 18	18
6			22
8			26

Remember:
Use the output from the first machine as the input for the second.

Or in a table:

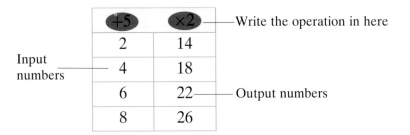

Write the operation in here

+5	×2
2	14
4	18
6	22
8	26

Input numbers

Output numbers

Exercise 5D

Copy and complete these tables:

(a)

+1	×2
1	4
2	
3	8
4	
5	

(b)

×2	+5
1	
2	9
3	
4	13
5	

(c)

÷2	+3
8	
12	
16	
20	
24	

(d)

÷5	×2
5	
10	
15	
20	
25	

(e)

−3	×3
3	
4	
5	
6	
7	

(f)

−6	×4
10	
11	
12	
13	
14	

(g)

+5	+7
0	
2	
4	
6	
8	

(h)

×2	×3
1	
2	
3	
4	
5	

(i)

−4	×10
4	
5	
6	
7	
8	

(j)

÷3	÷2
6	
12	
18	
24	
30	

(k)

−4	÷2
6	
8	
10	
12	
14	

(l)

×3	+6
2	
4	
6	
8	
10	

(m)

+5	−9
5	
6	
7	
8	
9	

(n)

−5	+9
10	
12	
14	
16	
18	

(o)

−2	÷6
14	
20	
26	
32	
38	

5.3 Inverse operations

If you know the output numbers from a number machine you can find the input numbers by using an **inverse operation**.

■ **An inverse operation 'undoes' the original operation:**

operation	inverse
+	−
−	+
×	÷
÷	×

Example 3

What are the inverse operations for:

(a) +6   (b) ÷3

(a) The opposite of + is −
    The inverse operation for +6 is −6
(b) The opposite of ÷ is ×
    The inverse operation for ÷3 is ×3

Example 4

Copy and complete the table by using inverses.

+5	
5	10
	11
	12
8	13
	14

The inverse of +5 is −5.

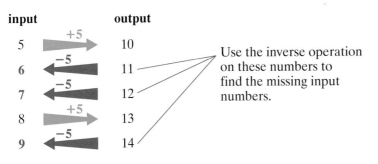

Use the inverse operation on these numbers to find the missing input numbers.

Exercise 5E

1 Write each operation and its inverse.
   (a) +6   (b) ×5   (c) −8   (d) ÷15   (e) +2
   (f) ÷9   (g) ×21   (h) −16   (i) −4   (j) +17

2 Copy and complete each table by using inverses.

(a)

+3	
3	6
	9
9	12
	15
	18

(b)

−4	
	0
	4
12	8
16	12
	16

(c)

+6	
1	7
	8
	9
4	10
	11

(d)

+10	
5	15
	16
	17
	18
	19

(e)

×2	
	6
4	8
	10
	12
	14

(f)

×5	
	35
8	40
	45
	50
	55

(g)

÷2	
4	2
	3
	4
	5
	6

(h)

−10	
	5
16	6
	7
	8
	9

(i)

×10	
	40
5	50
	60
	70
	80

(j)

÷5	
10	2
	3
20	4
	5
	6

(k)

÷3	
9	3
12	
	5
18	
	7

(l)

−7	
9	2
	3
11	
	5
	6

(m)

	×9
	27
	29
	31
	33
	35

(n)

	÷9
	5
	6
	7
	8
81	9

(o)

	×11
	22
	33
	44
5	
6	

(p)

	÷7
7	
14	
	3
	4
	5

(q)

	÷4
20	
	6
28	
	8
	9

(r)

	×9
	9
2	
	27
	36
	45

5.4 Number sequences and series

Look at the table:

The input numbers go up by 1 each time ...

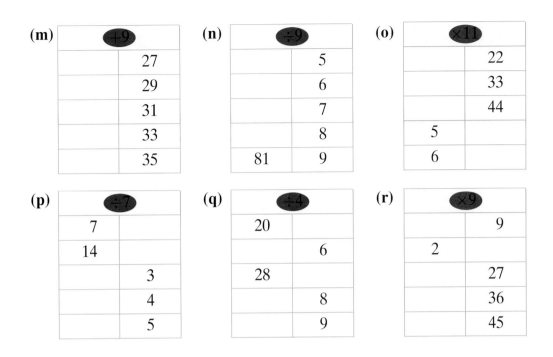

	×4
1	4
2	8
3	12
4	16
5	20

... the output numbers go up by 4 each time

So you can continue the output pattern without using the number machine each time:

$$\overset{+4}{\frown}\ \overset{+4}{\frown}\ \overset{+4}{\frown}\ \overset{+4}{\frown}$$
4   8   12   16   20

The next two numbers would be:

$$\overset{+4}{\frown}\ \overset{+4}{\frown}\ \overset{+4}{\frown}$$
16   20   **24**   **28**

The rule for the output numbers is 'add 4'.

■ **If you put a number pattern into a number machine you get a number pattern out.**

Example 5

For each sequence write down:

- the rule
- the next two numbers

(a) 1, 4, 7, 10, 13, . . . , . . .   **(b)** 15, 13, 11, 9, 7, . . . , . . .

(a) The numbers go up by 3 each time.

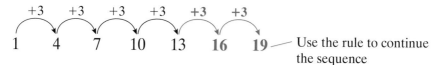

The rule is 'add 3'
The next two numbers are 16 and 19

(b) The numbers go down by 2 each time:

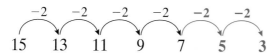

The rule is 'take away 2'
The next two numbers are 5 and 3

Exercise 5F

1 For each sequence write down:
- the rule
- the next two numbers

(a) 0, 2, 4, 6, 8, . . . , . . .   **(b)** 4, 8, 12, 16, . . . , . . .

(c) 7, 14, 21, 28, . . . , . . .   **(d)** 1, 4, 7, 10, . . . , . . .

(e) 100, 90, 80, 70, . . . , . . . **(f)** 30, 27, 24, 21, . . . , . . .

(g) 54, 51, 48, 45, . . . , . . .   **(h)** 54, 45, 36, . . . , . . .

(i) 15, 30, 45, . . . , . . .   **(j)** 100, 80, . . . , . . . , 20

(k) 100, 95, 90, . . . , . . .   **(l)** 27, 25, 23, . . . , . . .

(m) 2, 6, . . . , . . . , 18, 22   **(n)** 2, 5, 8, . . . , . . . , 17

(o) 5, 9, 13, . . . , . . .   **(p)** 20, 17, 14, 11, . . . , . . .

(q) 36, 30, 24, . . . , . . .   **(r)** 1, 2, 4, 7, 11, . . . , . . .

(s) 3, 6, 12, 24, . . . , . . .   **(t)** 1, 5, 25, . . . , . . .

Hint: If the numbers get bigger you are adding or multiplying. If the numbers get smaller you are subtracting or dividing.

(u) 2, 6, 18, …, …   **(v)** 1, 2, 4, 8, …, …

(w) 2000, 1000, 500, …, … **(x)** 243, 81, 27, …, …   Hint: (look at division)

(y) 24, 12, 6, …, …   **(z)** 64, 32, …, …, 4, 2

Summary of key points

1 You can use number machines to make number patterns.

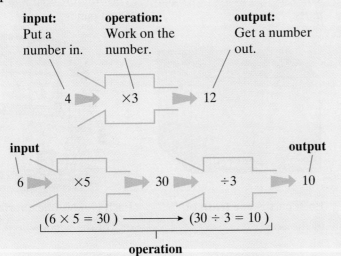

2 An inverse operation 'undoes' the original operation.

operation	inverse
+	−
−	+
×	÷
÷	×

3 If you put a number pattern into a number machine you get a number pattern out.

6 Fractions

6.1 Fractions all around

You can use fractions to describe things that are divided into equal parts:

Three friends share a stick of rock equally:

This box is split into ten equal parts:

This window is split into four equal panes:

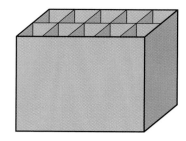

Each of them gets **one third** or $\frac{1}{3}$ of the rock.

Each part is **one tenth** or $\frac{1}{10}$ of the box.

Each pane is **one quarter** or $\frac{1}{4}$ of the window.

Geri has cleaned three window panes.
This is three quarters, or $\frac{3}{4}$ of the window:

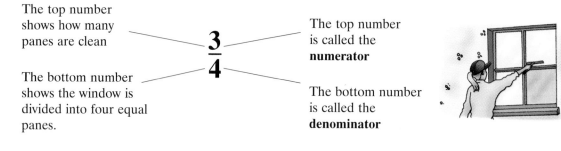

The top number shows how many panes are clean

The bottom number shows the window is divided into four equal panes.

$$\frac{3}{4}$$

The top number is called the **numerator**

The bottom number is called the **denominator**

Example 1

What fraction of this shape is shaded?
Write your answer in numbers and words.

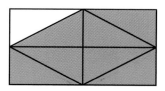

The shape has eight equal sized parts so each part is one eighth. Seven parts are shaded so the fraction shaded is seven eighths or $\frac{7}{8}$.

Exercise 6A

1   For each of these shapes:
   ● what fraction is shaded
   ● what fraction is **not** shaded
   Write your answers in words and numbers.

(a)   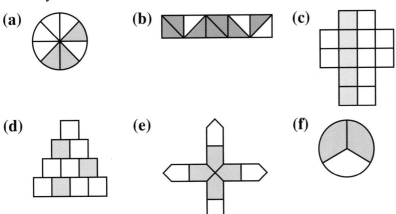   **(b)**   **(c)**

(d)   **(e)**   **(f)**

2   Write these fractions in words:

   (a) $\frac{1}{5}$ **(b)** $\frac{2}{3}$ **(c)** $\frac{3}{4}$ **(d)** $\frac{3}{5}$ **(e)** $\frac{1}{10}$

3   Write these fractions in numbers:
   (a) three eighths   **(b)** one thirteenth
   (c) four fifths   **(d)** two ninths

4   What fraction of each shape is shaded?

   (a)   **(b)**

   (c)   **(d)**

   (e)   **(f)**

   What do you notice? (**Hint**: compare your answers to
   (a) and **(b)**.)

6.2 Mixed numbers and improper fractions

Sometimes whole numbers and fractions are combined:

Here are $1\frac{1}{2}$ apple pies

This is the same as 3 *half* apple pies:

$$\frac{1}{2} + \frac{1}{2} + \frac{1}{2} = \frac{3}{2}$$

- ■ $1\frac{1}{2}$ **is a mixed number – it has a whole number part and a fraction part.**

- ■ $\frac{3}{2}$ **is an improper fraction – its numerator is greater than its denominator.**

- ■ **You can write a mixed number as an improper fraction. For example:** $1\frac{1}{2}$ **is equal to** $\frac{3}{2}$

Example 2

John buys five halves of water melon.

Write this as an improper fraction and as a mixed number.

You can write five halves as an:

- **improper fraction** $\quad \frac{1}{2} + \frac{1}{2} + \frac{1}{2} + \frac{1}{2} + \frac{1}{2} = \frac{5}{2}$

$$\frac{2}{2} + \frac{2}{2} + \frac{1}{2}$$

- **mixed number** $\qquad\quad 1 \;+\; 1 \;+\; \frac{1}{2} = 2\frac{1}{2}$

> Any fraction with its numerator and denominator the same is equal to 1:
> $1 = \frac{1}{1} = \frac{2}{2} = \frac{3}{3} \cdots$
> ... and so on.

Example 3

Mario sells chocolate cakes on his stall. At the end of a day
he has one and a quarter cakes left.
Write this as an improper fraction.

You write one and a quarter as $1\frac{1}{4}$:

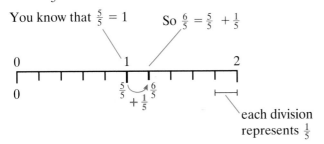

$$\frac{1}{4} + \frac{1}{4} + \frac{1}{4} + \frac{1}{4} + \frac{1}{4} = \frac{5}{4} \quad \textbf{improper fraction}$$

Remember:
$$1 = \frac{4}{4}$$
$$= \frac{1}{4} + \frac{1}{4} + \frac{1}{4} + \frac{1}{4}$$

There is more about
adding fractions on
page 97.

Example 4

Mark $\frac{6}{5}$ on a number line:

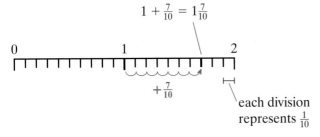

Example 5

Mark $1\frac{7}{10}$ on a number line.

$$1 + \frac{7}{10} = 1\frac{7}{10}$$

each division
represents $\frac{1}{10}$

Exercise 6B

1   Copy and complete:
   (a) $1 = \frac{1}{1} = \frac{}{2} = \frac{3}{} = \frac{4}{4} = \frac{}{5}$
   (b) $\frac{1}{2} + \frac{1}{2} + \frac{1}{2} = \frac{}{2}$
   (c) $\frac{1}{3} + \frac{1}{3} + \frac{1}{3} + \frac{1}{3} = \frac{}{3}$

2 This picture represents the fraction $\frac{3}{2}$. Draw pictures to represent these fractions:

   (a) $\frac{7}{2}$ **(b)** $\frac{5}{4}$ **(c)** $\frac{4}{3}$

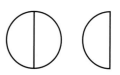

$\frac{3}{2}$ is 3 halves

3 For **(a)** to **(d)**, write the shaded amount as:
- a mixed number
- an improper fraction

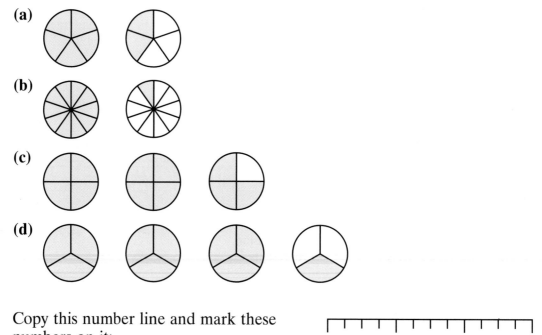

(a)

(b)

(c)

(d)

4 Copy this number line and mark these numbers on it:

   (a) $1\frac{1}{2}$ **(b)** two and a half   **(c)** $\frac{3}{4}$ **(d)** seven quarters

```
┌─┬─┬─┬─┬─┬─┬─┬─┬─┬─┬─┬─┐
0         1         2         3
```

5 Each mixed number in this box has a matching improper fraction. Write down the matching pairs like this: $1\frac{3}{5} = \frac{8}{5}$

$$1\frac{3}{5} \qquad \frac{8}{3} \qquad 2\frac{1}{4} \qquad \frac{8}{5} \qquad \frac{4}{3} \qquad 3\frac{1}{2} \qquad \frac{6}{5}$$

$$\frac{7}{6} \qquad 1\frac{1}{3} \qquad \frac{11}{6} \qquad 2\frac{2}{3}$$

$$\frac{9}{4} \qquad 1\frac{1}{5} \qquad 1\frac{5}{6} \qquad \frac{7}{2} \qquad 1\frac{1}{6}$$

6.3 Finding a fraction of a quantity

Sometimes you need to find a fraction of a quantity.

■   **You can think of the bottom part of a fraction as a division. For example:**

to find $\frac{1}{2}$ divide by 2
to find $\frac{1}{3}$ divide by 3
to find $\frac{1}{4}$ divide by 4

Example 6

Find $\frac{1}{3}$ of 30.

To find $\frac{1}{3}$ divide by 3.

$30 \div 3 = 10$ so $\frac{1}{3}$ of $30 = 10$

Example 7

Find $\frac{1}{5}$ of 20.

To find $\frac{1}{5}$ divide by 5.

$20 \div 5 = 4$ so $\frac{1}{5}$ of $20 = 4$

Example 8

Work out one half of £20.

To find $\frac{1}{2}$ divide by 2.

£$20 \div 2 = $ £10

so half of £20 is £10.

Example 9

Find one quarter of 20 km.

To find $\frac{1}{4}$ divide by 4.

$20 \text{ km} \div 4 = 5 \text{ km}$

so one quarter of 20 km is 5 km.

Exercise 6C

1   Work out:

(a) One third of
fifteen goldfish.

(b) One quarter of twelve
gingerbread men.

(c) One sixth of
eighteen videos.

2 Find:

   (a) $\frac{1}{2}$ of 24   **(b)** $\frac{1}{3}$ of 18   **(c)** $\frac{1}{10}$ of 90   **(d)** $\frac{1}{5}$ of 55

3 Find:

   (a) $\frac{1}{3}$ of 45 sweets   **(b)** $\frac{1}{6}$ of £30   **(c)** $\frac{1}{4}$ of 28 kg

   (d) $\frac{1}{7}$ of 14 hours   **(e)** $\frac{1}{15}$ of 60 p   **(f)** $\frac{1}{5}$ of 100 m

6.4 Finding more than one part

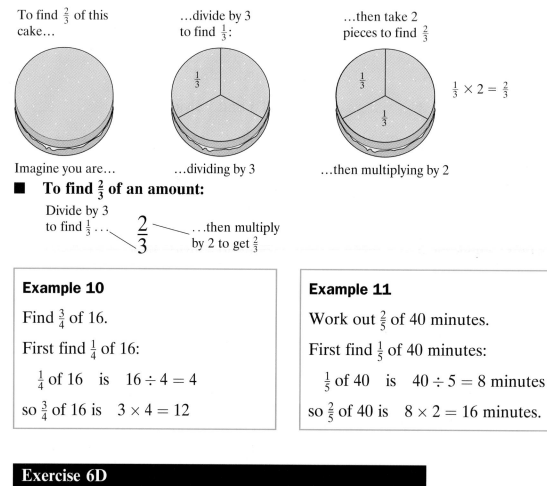

To find $\frac{2}{3}$ of this cake…   …divide by 3 to find $\frac{1}{3}$:   …then take 2 pieces to find $\frac{2}{3}$

$\frac{1}{3} \times 2 = \frac{2}{3}$

Imagine you are…   …dividing by 3   …then multiplying by 2

■ **To find $\frac{2}{3}$ of an amount:**

Divide by 3 to find $\frac{1}{3}$… $\dfrac{2}{3}$ …then multiply by 2 to get $\frac{2}{3}$

Example 10

Find $\frac{3}{4}$ of 16.

First find $\frac{1}{4}$ of 16:

   $\frac{1}{4}$ of 16   is $16 \div 4 = 4$

so $\frac{3}{4}$ of 16 is $3 \times 4 = 12$

Example 11

Work out $\frac{2}{5}$ of 40 minutes.

First find $\frac{1}{5}$ of 40 minutes:

   $\frac{1}{5}$ of 40   is $40 \div 5 = 8$ minutes

so $\frac{2}{5}$ of 40 is $8 \times 2 = 16$ minutes.

Exercise 6D

1 Work out:

   (a) $\frac{3}{5}$ of 15 books   **(b)** Two thirds of £30   **(c)** $\frac{5}{6}$ of 12 roses.

2 Find: **(a)** $\frac{3}{4}$ of 16 **(b)** $\frac{2}{3}$ of 33 **(c)** $\frac{3}{5}$ of 35 **(d)** $\frac{5}{6}$ of 60

3 Find: **(a)** $\frac{2}{3}$ of £15 **(b)** $\frac{3}{4}$ of 400 metres **(c)** $\frac{6}{7}$ of 42 minutes

4 Meena had 36 toffees, she ate five sixths of them. How many did she eat?

5 Twenty four pupils went for a picnic. Two eighths of them drank lemonade and one quarter drank orangeade.
   (a) How many drank lemonade?
   (b) How many drank orangeade?
   (c) What do you notice about your answers?

6 What is $\frac{4}{10}$ of:
   (a) 30 **(b)** 50 **(c)** 10 **(d)** 100

7 Sue gets £6 pocket money each week. She spends $\frac{2}{3}$ of her money on magazines and $\frac{3}{10}$ of her money on snacks.
   (a) How much does Sue spend on magazines?
   (b) How much does she spend on snacks?
   (c) How much money is left?

8 Vijay's car travelled 2000 miles last year. $\frac{3}{5}$ of this mileage was for work. How many miles did he travel for work?

6.5 Equivalent fractions

You can cut this cake into . . .

. . . halves   . . . quarters 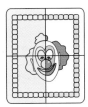   . . . tenths

Notice that:

$\frac{1}{2}$ is the same as $\frac{2}{4}$ is the same as $\frac{5}{10}$

$\frac{1}{2}$, $\frac{2}{4}$ and $\frac{5}{10}$ all represent the same amount.

They are all **equivalent fractions**.

- **Equivalent fractions have the same value.**

  For example: $\frac{2}{3} = \frac{4}{6} = \frac{12}{18}$

  Equivalent just means having the same value.

- **You can find equivalent fractions by multiplying the numerator and denominator by the same number.**

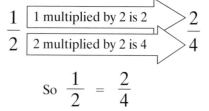

$$\text{So } \frac{1}{2} = \frac{2}{4}$$

- **You can find equivalent fractions by dividing the numerator and denominator by the same number.**

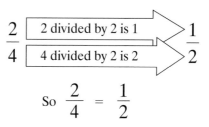

$$\text{So } \frac{2}{4} = \frac{1}{2}$$

$\frac{1}{2}$ is the **simplest form** of the fraction $\frac{2}{4}$
There is no equivalent fraction with smaller numbers on the top and bottom.

Dividing top and bottom by the same number is called **cancelling**.

Example 12

Find the missing numbers that make these fractions equivalent:

(a) $\dfrac{1}{2} = \dfrac{\square}{8}$

(b) $\dfrac{2}{14} = \dfrac{1}{\square}$

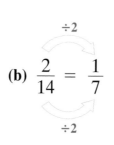

(a) $\dfrac{1}{2} = \dfrac{4}{8}$

(b) $\dfrac{2}{14} = \dfrac{1}{7}$

Notice that 2 is a **factor** *of 2 and 14. There is more about factors on page 49.*

Example 13

How many sixths are equivalent to $\frac{1}{3}$?

Multiply the top and bottom by 2:

$$\frac{1}{3} = \frac{2}{6}$$

So $\frac{2}{6}$ is equivalent to $\frac{1}{3}$

Example 14

Which is larger, $\frac{3}{5}$ or $\frac{7}{10}$?

Find an equivalent fraction in tenths for $\frac{3}{5}$:

$$\frac{3}{5} = \frac{6}{10}$$

$\frac{3}{5}$ is equivalent to $\frac{6}{10}$, so $\frac{7}{10}$ is larger than $\frac{3}{5}$.

Exercise 6E

1   Find an equivalent fraction for:
    (a) $\frac{2}{3}$ in sixths   (b) $\frac{3}{5}$ in tenths

2   Find the missing numbers that make these fractions equivalent:

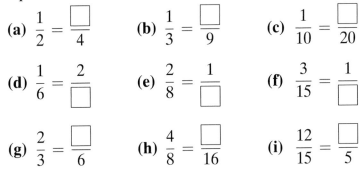

(a) $\frac{1}{2} = \frac{\square}{4}$ (b) $\frac{1}{3} = \frac{\square}{9}$ (c) $\frac{1}{10} = \frac{\square}{20}$

(d) $\frac{1}{6} = \frac{2}{\square}$ (e) $\frac{2}{8} = \frac{1}{\square}$ (f) $\frac{3}{15} = \frac{1}{\square}$

(g) $\frac{2}{3} = \frac{\square}{6}$ (h) $\frac{4}{8} = \frac{\square}{16}$ (i) $\frac{12}{15} = \frac{\square}{5}$

3 Which is larger, $\frac{1}{5}$ or $\frac{3}{10}$?

4 Sangeeta and Ryan each win the same amount of money in a prize draw. Ryan spends one fifth of his money. Sangeeta spends four twentieths of hers. Who spends the most? Explain your answer.

5 Find the pairs of equivalent fractions in this box. Write them down like this: $\frac{1}{2} = \frac{6}{12}$

$$\frac{1}{2} \quad \frac{4}{5} \quad \frac{1}{3}$$
$$\frac{1}{5}$$
$$\frac{6}{10} \quad \frac{4}{7} \quad \frac{6}{30} \quad \frac{3}{5}$$
$$\frac{8}{14} \quad \frac{4}{12}$$
$$\frac{20}{25} \quad \frac{6}{12}$$

6 Which of these fractions are less than $\frac{1}{2}$?

$$\frac{3}{5} \quad \frac{1}{20} \quad \frac{2}{10} \quad \frac{9}{20} \quad \frac{30}{100}$$

7 Find the pairs of equivalent fractions in this box:

$$\frac{1}{10} \quad \frac{75}{100} \quad \frac{2}{10} \quad \frac{25}{100}$$
$$\frac{5}{10} \quad \frac{50}{100}$$
$$\frac{20}{100} \quad \frac{10}{100} \quad \frac{1}{4} \quad \frac{3}{4}$$

Hint:
$1 \times 25 = 25$
$2 \times 25 = 50$
$3 \times 25 = 75$
$4 \times 25 = 100$

8 Write these fractions in their **simplest** form:

(a) $\frac{8}{16}$ **(b)** $\frac{3}{9}$ **(c)** $\frac{15}{20}$ **(d)** $\frac{80}{100}$

Remember:
The simplest form is the equivalent fraction with the smallest numbers possible on top and bottom.

6.6 Adding and subtracting fractions

It is easy to add or subtract fractions with the same denominator (bottom).

Example 15

(a) Work out $\frac{1}{3} + \frac{1}{3}$

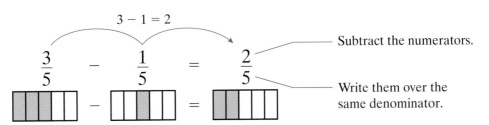

$$1 + 1 = 2$$

$$\frac{1}{3} + \frac{1}{3} = \frac{2}{3}$$

Add the numerators (top).

Write them over the same denominator (bottom).

(b) Work out $\frac{3}{5} - \frac{1}{5}$

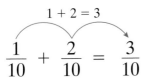

$$3 - 1 = 2$$

$$\frac{3}{5} - \frac{1}{5} = \frac{2}{5}$$

Subtract the numerators.

Write them over the same denominator.

■ **To add (or subtract) fractions with the same denominator add (or subtract) the numerators. Write the result over the same denominator.**

Example 16

Work out:

(a) $\frac{1}{10} + \frac{2}{10}$ **(b)** $\frac{7}{8} - \frac{3}{8}$

(a) Denominators are the same so add the numerators:

$$1 + 2 = 3$$

$$\frac{1}{10} + \frac{2}{10} = \frac{3}{10}$$

(b) Denominators are the same so subtract the numerators:

$$7 - 3 = 4$$

$$\frac{7}{8} - \frac{3}{8} = \frac{4}{8}$$

Exercise 6F

1 Add these fractions:

    (a) $\frac{1}{3} + \frac{1}{3}$ **(b)** $\frac{2}{5} + \frac{1}{5}$ **(c)** $\frac{3}{10} + \frac{4}{10}$ **(d)** $\frac{10}{100} + \frac{15}{100}$

2 Work out these subtractions:

    (a) $\frac{4}{7} - \frac{2}{7}$ **(b)** $\frac{3}{3} - \frac{1}{3}$ **(c)** $\frac{9}{12} - \frac{6}{12}$ **(d)** $\frac{20}{100} - \frac{5}{100}$

3 Add these fractions and write each answer in its simplest form.

    (a) $\frac{1}{6} + \frac{2}{6}$ **(b)** $\frac{3}{8} + \frac{1}{8}$ **(c)** $\frac{3}{12} + \frac{5}{12}$ **(d)** $\frac{1}{10} + \frac{3}{10}$

> There is more about simplest form on page 94.

4 Do these subtractions and write your answers in simplest form.

    (a) $\frac{4}{9} - \frac{1}{9}$ **(b)** $\frac{4}{10} - \frac{2}{10}$ **(c)** $1 - \frac{2}{6}$ **(d)** $1 - \frac{4}{10}$

> Remember:
> $1 = \frac{1}{1} = \frac{2}{2} \ldots$

5 Kay had $\frac{3}{5}$ metres of silk. She gave $\frac{1}{5}$ metres to Aisling. How much did she have left?

6 On his way to school Selim spends $\frac{4}{8}$ of the journey in a bus and $\frac{3}{8}$ of the journey in a train.
    Then he walks the rest of the way.

    (a) What fraction of the journey is spent altogether on the train and the bus?
    (b) What fraction did he walk?

7 Surmey bought $\frac{1}{10}$ kg of grapes, $\frac{3}{10}$ kg of apples and $\frac{2}{10}$ kg of plums. How much did the fruit weigh altogether?

Summary of key points

1 You can use numbers to represent a fraction:

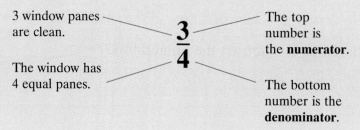

3 window panes are clean. — $\dfrac{3}{4}$ — The top number is the **numerator**.

The window has 4 equal panes. — The bottom number is the **denominator**.

2 An improper fraction has a numerator greater than its denominator, for example $\frac{3}{2}$

3 A mixed number has a whole number part and a fraction part, for example $1\frac{1}{2}$

4 You can write a mixed number as an improper fraction, for example:

$1\frac{1}{2}$ is equal to $\frac{3}{2}$

5 You can think of the bottom part of a fraction as a division. For example:

to find $\frac{1}{2}$ divide by 2

to find $\frac{1}{3}$ divide by 3

to find $\frac{1}{4}$ divide by 4

6 To find $\frac{2}{3}$ of an amount:

Divide by 3
to find $\frac{1}{3}$ ... $\frac{2}{3}$ ... then multiply by 2 to get $\frac{2}{3}$

7 Equivalent fractions have the same value.

For example: $\frac{2}{3} = \frac{4}{6} = \frac{12}{18}$

8 You can find equivalent fractions by multiplying (or dividing) the numerator and denominator by the same number.

$\div 2$

$$\frac{4}{6} = \frac{2}{3}$$

$\div 2$

9 To add or subtract fractions with the same denominator add or subtract the numerators. Write the result over the same denominator.

7 Probability

What are your chances of ...

... tossing a head?

"fifty-fifty"

... being struck by lightning?

"1 in 200 000"

... winning the jackpot?

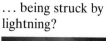

"1 in 14 million"

... solving Fermat's last theorem?

Andrew Wiles proved it in 1994

Probability uses numbers to represent the chance or likelihood that something will happen.

7.1 The language of probability

The likelihood of something happening can be described as **impossible**, **possible** or **certain**:

It is **impossible** for you to see a living dinosaur.

It is **possible** that either team will win.

It is **certain** that there will be a full moon this year.

Some things are more likely to happen than others.

Impossible	Unlikely	Even chance	Likely	Certain
No chance of happening	More chance of not happening than happening	Equally likely to happen or not happen	More chance of happening than not happening	Will happen

It is **likely** that it will be warm in Lanzarote in December.

It is **unlikely** that it will be warm in Brighton in December.

Example 1

Write down whether these statements are certain, possible or impossible.

Give a reason for your answer.

(a) A hedgehog will hibernate.

(b) A person will grow wings.

(c) It will snow in Liverpool in December.

(a) It is certain that a hedgehog will hibernate, as they do this to survive the winter.

(b) It is impossible for a person to grow wings.

(c) It is possible that it will snow in Liverpool in December as it is winter time.

Example 2

Say whether each of the following are likely or unlikely, giving reasons.

If you pick a number from 1 to 5 at random:

(a) You will pick a prime number.

(b) You will pick an odd number.

(c) You will pick a number less than 2.

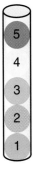

(a) This is likely as the numbers 2, 3 and 5 are all prime.

(b) This is likely because the numbers 1, 3 and 5 are all odd.

(c) This is unlikely because only number 1 is less than 2.

Exercise 7A

1   Write down whether these statements are certain, possible or impossible, giving reasons.
   (a) You will see the sea this year.
   (b) You will turn on a light today.
   (c) You will eat a worm tomorrow.
   (d) Your brother will drive a car this week.
   (e) The tide will come in each day.
   (f) You will feed a cat today.
   (g) A cook will break eggs to make an omelette.

2   Is each statement likely or unlikely? Give a reason for your answer.
   (a) Your family will win the lottery this year.
   (b) You will swim 100 metres this week.
   (c) You will get on a bus this week.

3.   Copy this table:

Outcomes			
Impossible	Unlikely	Likely	Certain

Fill in two impossible, two unlikely, two likely and two certain statements.

7.2 The likelihood scale

You can show how likely it is that something will happen on a **likelihood scale**:

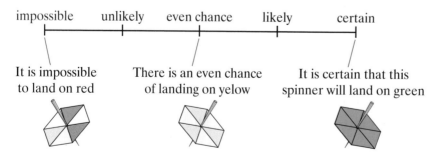

impossible   unlikely   even chance   likely   certain

It is impossible
to land on red

There is an even chance
of landing on yelow

It is certain that this
spinner will land on green

Example 3

Draw a likelihood scale.
Mark on it the likelihood that:

(a) A tossed coin will land on heads.

(b) You can use a magnet to pick up paper.

(c) It will rain in London this year.

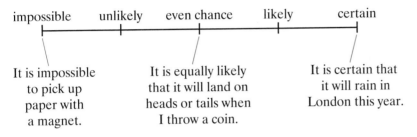

■ **A likelihood scale runs from impossible to certain with even chance in the middle.**

Exercise 7B

1   Draw a likelihood scale. Mark on it the likelihood that:
   (a) Steam will rise from boiling water.
   (b) A unicorn will be in your classroom.
   (c) You will walk 5 kilometres today.
   (d) You will drink tea today.
   (e) You will watch television tomorrow.

2   Copy this likelihood scale and mark on something to match the likelihood of A, B, C and D.

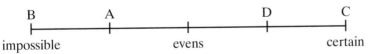

7.3 Using numbers to represent probabilities

You can use numbers to show how likely it is that something will happen.

■ **Probability uses numbers to represent the chance that something will happen.**

■ **All probabilities have a value from 0 to 1.**

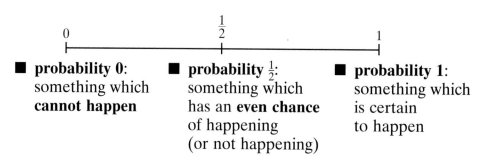

■ **probability 0**:
something which
cannot happen

■ **probability $\frac{1}{2}$**:
something which
has an **even chance**
of happening
(or not happening)

■ **probability 1**:
something which
is certain
to happen

Example 4

Mark these on a probability scale.
Give a reason for your answer.

(a) It will not rain in Manchester in October.
(b) A person will grow horns.
(c) April Fool's Day will fall on the first of April.
(d) The letter A is picked at random from the letters
ABBA.

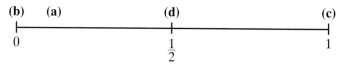

(a) is unlikely as it will probably rain at least once in October.
(b) is impossible.
(c) is certain.
(d) is evens, there is the same amount of letter A's and B's.

Exercise 7C

1   Mark these on a probability scale. Give reasons for
your answers.

  (a) You will get an even number when you roll a fair dice.
  (b) You will be younger tomorrow.
  (c) Your birthday will fall at the weekend this year.
  (d) You will eat crisps tomorrow.
  (e) A female cat will give birth to another female cat.

2   One of these four letter tiles is picked at random.
Mark on a probability scale the probability that:

  (a) A vowel is picked.
  (b) Letter A is picked.
  (c) Letter R is picked.
  (d) A letter worth 1 point is picked.
  (e) A letter worth 10 points is picked.

7.4 Events and outcomes

There is a difference between an **event** and an **outcome**.

At the start of some games a dice is rolled to decide who will start.

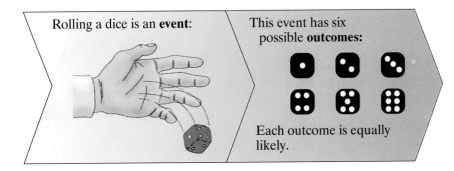

Rolling a dice is an **event**:

This event has six possible **outcomes**:

Each outcome is equally likely.

■ **When outcomes of an event have the same chance of happening, they are equally likely.**

Sometimes a coin is used to decide who shall start a game.

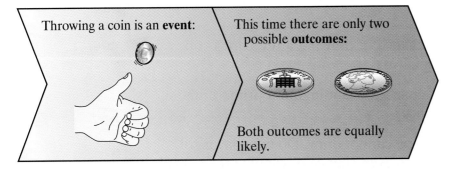

Throwing a coin is an **event**:

This time there are only two possible **outcomes**:

Both outcomes are equally likely.

■ **When there are two equally likely outcomes of an event, each outcome has an even chance of happening.**

Example 5

Leo rolls a dice.

(a) List all the possible outcomes.
(b) Is there an even chance of getting an odd number?

(a) 1, 2, 3, 4, 5 and 6.
(b) Yes, the chance of getting an odd number is evens. There are 3 odd and 3 even numbers on the die, so there are two equally likely outcomes odd or even.

Example 6

List the possible outcomes for this spinner.

There are eight equally likely outcomes. They are red, yellow, blue, orange, white, light blue, black and purple.

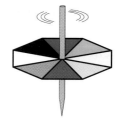

Example 7

There are 100 letter tiles in this game. Forty-two are vowels and two are blanks. Is there an even chance of picking a consonant tile?

There are 56 consonants and 44 others, so there are not two equally likely outcomes. This means there is not an even chance of picking a consonant tile.

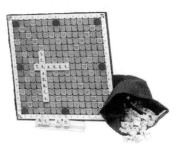

Exercise 7D

1 Is there an even chance that this spinner will land on white?

2 Is there an even chance of drawing a red card from a deck of playing cards?

3 Is there an even chance of landing on a prime number when you roll a dice?

4 In a squash game you cannot draw. Do two players of identical skill have an even chance of winning the game?

5 If the two equally likely outcomes for Hurricanes' next shot are he pots it or he doesn't pot it, do you think Hurricane has an even chance of winning this shot?

6 Abena chooses a number from 1 to 7 at random.
   (a) List all the equally possible outcomes.
   (b) Is there an even chance of choosing an odd number?

7 List all the equally likely outcomes for this spinner.

8 If you pick a card from a deck of playing cards:
   (a) How many possible outcomes are there?
   (b) List the equally likely suits you could pick.
   (c) What are the equally likely colours you might pick?

7.5 Calculating probabilities with one successful outcome

Sometimes you can calculate the probability that something will happen.

Throwing a dice has six possible outcomes:

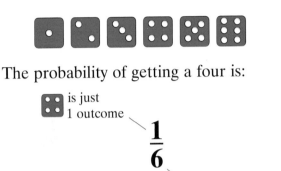

The probability of getting a four is:

is just
1 outcome

$$\frac{1}{6}$$

there are 6
possible outcomes

Example 8

Write the probability of the number 8 coming out first in the lottery.

Each number has an equal chance of being chosen.
There are 49 possible outcomes for the first ball.
There is only one number 8, so the probability is 1/49.

Exercise 7E

Write the probability of:

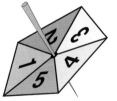

1 rolling the number 3 on an ordinary dice
2 getting the number 5 on this spinner
3 getting tails when throwing a coin
4 choosing the ace of hearts from a pack of ordinary cards
5 getting a number 7 when you roll a 12-sided dice
6 a male being the next person to enter the room
7 choosing a letter S from the letters W A R S A W
8 the white dog being put in trap number one

9 the white dog being put in trap seven
10 the white dog winning, if all dogs have the same chance of winning.

7.6 Calculating probabilities with more than one successful outcome

Sometimes you need to calculate the probability of an event with more than one successful outcome.

When you roll a dice, there are six possible outcomes.

There are three odd numbers on a dice.

The probability of getting an odd number is:

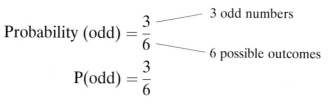

$$\text{Probability (odd)} = \frac{3}{6}$$

or

$$P(\text{odd}) = \frac{3}{6}$$

■ **The probability that an event will happen is:**

$$P(\text{event}) = \frac{\text{the number of successful outcomes}}{\text{total number of possible outcomes}}$$

Example 9

Calculate the probability of:
(a) picking a vowel from the letters of the alphabet
(b) picking a consonant from the letters of the alphabet
(c) picking a number less than 10 from the numbers 1 to 50.

(a) There are 5 vowels in the 26 letters of the alphabet so:
probability (picking vowel) $= \frac{5}{26}$ or
P (picking vowel) $= \frac{5}{26}$.
(b) There are 21 consonants in the 26 letters of the alphabet so:
probability (picking consonant) $= \frac{21}{26}$ or
P (picking consonant) $= \frac{21}{26}$.
(c) There are 9 numbers less than 10 in the numbers 1 to 50 so:
probability (picking number less than 10) $= \frac{9}{50}$ or
P (less than 10) $= \frac{9}{50}$.

Example 10

These 5 footballers are wearing differing kits. If one is chosen to play at random, calculate the probability it will be:

(a) A person in blue and white

(b) Someone with black hair

(c) Someone with a striped top

(a) Two of the five players are wearing blue and white so

probability (blue and white) $= \frac{2}{5}$ or

P(blue and white) $= \frac{2}{5}$.

(b) Three players have black hair so:

probability (black hair) $= \frac{3}{5}$ or

P(black hair) $= \frac{3}{5}$.

(c) Four players have striped tops so:

probability (striped tops) $= \frac{4}{5}$ or

P(striped tops) $= \frac{4}{5}$.

Exercise 7F

1 John is playing a game with some of his friends.
They each take turns to pick one of these counters from a bag at random.
What is the probability that they will pick:.

(a) a blue counter.

(b) an even numbered counter.

(c) an odd numbered counter.

(d) a purple counter.

(e) a green counter.

(f) a counter numbered higher than 10.

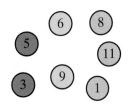

2   Duncan brings in a tray of food and drinks.
John picks something from the tray at random.
Write the probability that he will choose:

    (a) a yellow cake

    (b) a cola drink

    (c) an orange drink

    (d) a brown cake

    (e) a purple cake

3   Two children decide to play with an ordinary
pack of cards. They take the first card from
the top of the pack.

Write the probability that it will be:

    (a) a seven

    (b) a spade

    (c) a red card

    (d) a picture card (king, queen or Jack)

    (e) a diamond or a club

    (f) a heart, diamond, club or spade

    (g) a blank card.

Summary of key points

1   A likelihood scale runs from impossible to certain with even chance in the middle.

2   Probability uses numbers to represent the chance that something will happen.

3   All probabilities have a value from 0 to 1.

4

$$
\begin{array}{ccc}
0 & \frac{1}{2} & 1 \\
\vdash & \!\vdash & \!\dashv
\end{array}
$$

Something which cannot happen has a probability of 0.

Something which has an even chance of happening (or not happening) has a probability of $\frac{1}{2}$.

Something which is certain to happen has a probability of 1.

5 When outcomes of an event have the same chance of happening, they are equally likely.

6 When there are two equally likely outcomes of an event, each outcome has an even chance of happening.

7 The probability that an event will happen is:

$$P(\text{event}) = \frac{\text{the number of successful outcomes}}{\text{total number of possible outcomes}}$$

8 Decimals and percentages

8.1 Decimal numbers

The winner took 63.57 seconds to finish this race.

63.57 is a **decimal number**.

- **In a decimal number the decimal point separates the whole number from the part that is less than one.**

decimal point

63.57

63 is the whole number part

.57 is the part less than one

This place value diagram shows what the digits in 63.57 mean:

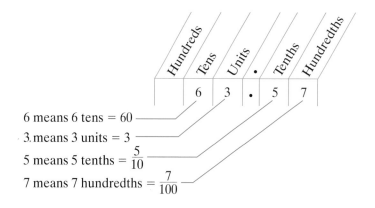

6 means 6 tens = 60

3. means 3 units = 3

5 means 5 tenths = $\frac{5}{10}$

7 means 7 hundredths = $\frac{7}{100}$

You say 'sixty three point five seven'.

Example 1

This parcel weighs 3.75 kg

(a) Show the number 3.75 on a place value diagram.
(b) Write down the value of each digit.

(a)

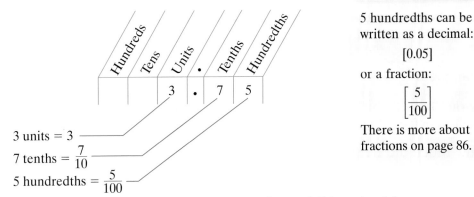

3 units = 3
7 tenths = $\frac{7}{10}$
5 hundredths = $\frac{5}{100}$

5 hundredths can be written as a decimal:

[0.05]

or a fraction:

$$\left[\frac{5}{100}\right]$$

There is more about fractions on page 86.

(b) The values of the digits are: 3 units, 7 tenths and 5 hundredths.

Example 2

Write down the value of the underlined digit in each decimal number:

(a) 7<u>3</u>.6   (b) 2.8<u>6</u>   (c) 2.<u>0</u>5   (d) 0.2<u>6</u>

Write .26 as 0.26
The zero draws attention to the decimal point.

(a) 3 units   (b) 6 hundredths
(c) 0 tenths   (d) 6 hundredths

Exercise 8A

1 Show these numbers on a place value diagram:

(a) Calculator   28.2   C = ÷ ×
(b) Calculator   129.57   C = ÷ ×
(c) Calculator   53.02   C = ÷ ×

2 Show these numbers on a place value diagram.

(a) 23.4   (b) 5.42   (c) 47.6   (d) 563.8   (e) 2.94   (f) 0.67
(g) 4.06   (h) 47.08 (i) 0.08   (j) 830.06 (k) 29.73 (l) 0.04

3 Write down the value of the underlined digit in each number:

(a) 4<u>8</u>.9   (b) 5<u>7</u>.4   (c) 28.7<u>6</u>   (d) 4.<u>9</u>2   (e) 22.8<u>4</u>   (f) 9.<u>2</u>5
(g) <u>7</u>38.9 (h) 5<u>7</u>2.8 (i) 8.2<u>9</u>   (j) 4.<u>6</u>3   (k) 8.3<u>4</u>   (l) 0.0<u>8</u>

8.2 Adding and subtracting decimals

You can add decimal numbers in the same way as you add amounts of money in pounds and pence.

■ **When adding or subtracting with decimals, always line up the decimal points.**

Example 3

Kwong buys a shirt for £17.25 and a sweater for £22.62.

How much did he pay in total?

To find £17.25 + £22.62:

$$
\begin{array}{r}
17{.}25 \\
22{.}62 \\
\hline
\end{array}
$$

Line up the decimal points. This lines up the units.

Put the point in the answer.

$$
\begin{array}{r}
17.25 \\
+\ 22.62 \\
\hline
39.87 \\
\end{array}
$$

Then add.

The answer is £39.87

> Remember to add the numbers in the right hand column first.
> There is more about adding on page 22.

Example 4

The temperature in Preston at midnight was 13.6°C.
By noon the temperature had risen by 5.8°C.
What was the temperature at noon?

To find 13.6°C + 5.8°C:

$$
\begin{array}{r}
13.6 \\
+\ \ 5.8 \\
\hline
19.4 \\
\end{array}
$$

Line up the decimal points and add:

So the temperature at noon was 19.4°C.

Exercise 8B

1   Work out:
(a) £32.53 + £24.05   (b) £5.40 + £14.37   (c) £2.30 + £7.60
(d) £8.42 + £6.35   (e) £57.36 + £18.44   (f) £16.39 + £37.24

2   Work out:
(a) 4.2 + 1.6   (b) 6 + 1.38   (c) 163.7 + 0.25
(d) 9.2 + 8.3   (e) 1.3 + 16.2 + 2.46   (f) 8.01 + 15 + 0.52

3   Work out:
(a) 3.6 + 1.5   (b) 7 + 9.26   (c) 243.7 + 0.46
(d) 7.8 + 6.4   (e) 5.7 + 6.2 + 2.4   (f) 6.51 + 14 + 0.73

4   The temperature in Barnet at midnight was 5.9°C.
By noon the next day the temperature had gone up
by 4.6°C.
What was the temperature in Barnet at noon?

5   Jenny's empty bag weighs 0.94 kg. She puts a book
weighing 1.05 kg and a pencil case weighing 0.43 kg in it.
What is the total weight of Jenny's bag and its contents?

Example 5

The temperature in Bristol at noon
was 29.8°C.
By midnight the temperature
was 15.5°C.

By how much did the temperature fall?

To find 29.8°C − 15.5°C:

Write out the   ... then take away
subtraction ...   as normal

$$
\begin{array}{r}
29.8 \\
-\ 15.5 \\
\hline
\end{array}
$$
Remember to
line up the
decimal points.

$$
\begin{array}{r}
29.8 \\
-\ 15.5 \\
\hline
14.3 \\
\end{array}
$$

There is more about
subtraction on
page 23.

The temperature in Bristol fell by 14.3°C.

Example 6

Natalie went shopping with £19.27. Afterwards she had £6.85 left. How much did she spend?

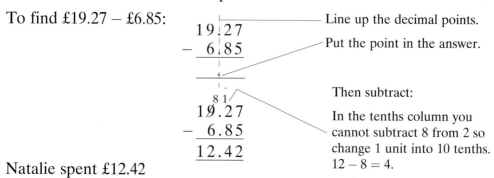

To find £19.27 − £6.85:

Line up the decimal points.

Put the point in the answer.

$$\begin{array}{r} 19.27 \\ -\ \ 6.85 \\ \hline \end{array}$$

$$\begin{array}{r} {}^{8}1\\ 1\!\!\!/9.27 \\ -\ \ 6.85 \\ \hline 12.42 \end{array}$$

Then subtract:

In the tenths column you cannot subtract 8 from 2 so change 1 unit into 10 tenths.
$12 - 8 = 4.$

Natalie spent £12.42

Exercise 8C

Work out these subtractions. Show all your working.

1 **(a)** £5.94 − £3.82 **(b)** £3.49 − £1.26
  (c) £19.65 − £4.23 **(d)** £14.25 − £8.73

2 **(a)** 7.8 − 3.4 **(b)** 0.95 − 0.52 **(c)** 3.9 − 0.5
  (d) 14.7 − 3.4 **(e)** 9.47 − 4.23 **(f)** 16.86 − 4.35

3 **(a)** 230.8 − 3.4 **(b)** 0.92 − 0.56 **(c)** 2.3 − 0.6
  (d) 1 − 0.4 **(e)** 9.2 − 4.7 **(f)** 15.82 − 2.35

4 The temperature in London at noon was 18.3°C.
  By midnight the temperature had fallen by 5.2°C.
  What was the temperature in London at midnight?

5 A cake weighed 1.32 kg.
  What was the weight of the
  cake after Steve had eaten a
  slice that weighed 0.15 kg?

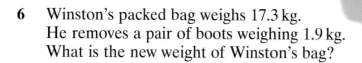

6 Winston's packed bag weighs 17.3 kg.
  He removes a pair of boots weighing 1.9 kg.
  What is the new weight of Winston's bag?

7 Sajida sawed a piece of wood 0.8 metres long from a
  piece 2.5 metres long. How much wood was left over?

8.3 Multiplying and dividing decimal numbers by 10, 100 and 1000

You can multiply and divide decimal numbers by 10, 100 and 1000 in the same way that you can divide whole numbers by 10, 100 and 1000.

Multiplying decimals by 10, 100 and 1000

■ **To multiply decimal numbers by 10 move the digits one place to the left.**

Example 7

Work out 34.6×10

3 tens $= 30$
$\qquad 30 \times 10 = 300$
4 units $= 4$
$\qquad 4 \times 10 = 40$
6 tenths $= 0.6$
$\qquad 0.6 \times 10 = 6$

so $34.6 \times 10 = 346$

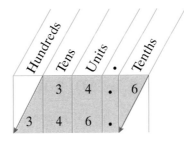

Similarly:

■ **To multiply decimal numbers by 100 move the digits two places to the left:**

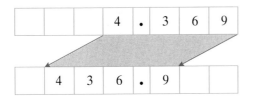

So $4.369 \times 100 = 436.9$

■ **To multiply decimal numbers by 1000 move the digits three places to the left:**

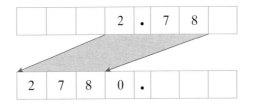

So $2.78 \times 1000 = 2780$

Example 8

Without using a calculator write down the answers to

(a) 63.58×10 **(b)** 5.94×100 **(c)** 3.6×1000

(a) $63.58 \times 10 = 635.8$ Move the digits 1 place to the left.

(b) $5.94 \times 100 = 594$ Move the digits 2 places to the left.

(c) $3.6 \times 1000 = 3600$ Move the digits 3 places to the left.

Exercise 8D

Write down the answers to these calculations:

1   **(a)** 4.74×10 **(b)** 23.5×10 **(c)** 0.503×10
    (d) 0.079×10 **(e)** 67.39×10 **(f)** 0.04×10

2   **(a)** 5.83×100 **(b)** 32.59×100 **(c)** 3.679×1000
    (d) 6.49×1000 **(e)** 45.8×100 **(f)** 0.07×1000

3   **(a)** 0.076×100 **(b)** 6.408×10 **(c)** 0.0303×100
    (d) 7.99×1000 **(e)** 8.47×10 **(f)** 0.0056×1000

4   **(a)** 89.3×100 **(b)** 6.38×1000 **(c)** 0.08×10
    (d) 0.034×100 **(e)** 83.65×10 **(f)** 29.3×1000

Dividing decimal numbers by 10, 100 and 1000

■ **To divide decimal numbers by 10 move the digits one place to the right.**

You can revise dividing with whole numbers on page 43.

Example 9

Work out $94.3 \div 10$.

   9 tens $= 90$

     $90 \div 10 = 9 = 9$ units

   4 units $= 4$

     $4 \div 10 = \frac{4}{10} = 0.4 = 4$ tenths

3 tenths $= \frac{3}{10}$

     $\frac{3}{10} \div 10 = 0.03 = 3$ hundredths

So $94.3 \div 10 = 9.43$

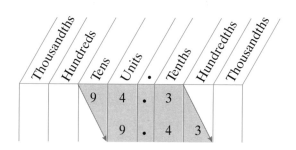

Similarly, for dividing decimal numbers by 100 and 1000:

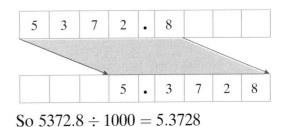

■ **To divide decimal numbers by 100 move the digits two places to the right:**

| 1 | 5 | 3 | 8 | . | 4 | | |

| | | 1 | 5 | . | 3 | 8 | 4 |

So $1538.4 \div 100 = 15.384$

■ **To divide decimal numbers by 1000 move the digits three places to the right:**

| 5 | 3 | 7 | 2 | . | 8 | | | |

| | | | 5 | . | 3 | 7 | 2 | 8 |

So $5372.8 \div 1000 = 5.3728$

Example 10

Without using a calculator work out:

(a) $865.6 \div 10$ (b) $26.37 \div 100$ (c) $83.7 \div 1000$

(a) $865.6 \div 10 = 86.56$

(b) $26.37 \div 100 = 0.2637$

(c) $83.7 \div 1000 = 0.0837$

Hint:
You must put the extra zero in here to say there are no tenths.

Exercise 8E

Do these questions without using a calculator.

1   (a) $29.6 \div 10$ (b) $286.5 \div 10$ (c) $3.95 \div 10$
      (d) $674.3 \div 10$ (e) $0.085 \div 10$ (f) $0.07 \div 10$

2   (a) $358.3 \div 10$ (b) $49.8 \div 10$ (c) $2963.5 \div 10$
      (d) $927.8 \div 100$ (e) $5.7 \div 100$ (f) $23.6 \div 1000$

3   (a) $95.3 \div 10$ (b) $264.7 \div 10$ (c) $3.9 \div 100$
      (d) $679 \div 1000$ (e) $385 \div 100$ (f) $47 \div 100$

4   (a) $28.6 \div 100$ (b) $0.79 \div 10$ (c) $2.9 \div 100$
      (d) $6.3 \div 1000$ (e) $0.06 \div 100$ (f) $53.9 \div 1000$

5   (a) 9.23×10 (b) $26.5 \div 10$ (c) $5.47 \div 1000$
      (d) 19.8×100 (e) $36.2 \div 100$ (f) 0.34×1000

8.4 Multiplying decimals by whole numbers

Example 11

Find the cost of 3 sandwiches
at £1.32 each.

$$
\begin{array}{r}
132 \\
\times\ \ 3 \\
\hline
396
\end{array}
$$

Multiply the numbers
together ignoring
the decimal point.

132 is 100 times 1.32, so 396 is
100 times the actual answer.
To find the actual answer
divide 396 by 100.

The cost of the sandwiches is £3.96

Notice that the answer and the original number have the
same number of digits after the decimal point:

$$132 \times 3 = 396$$
$$1.32 \times 3 = 3.96$$

Two digits on the right
of the decimal point.
The numbers have two decimal places.

■ **When you multiply a decimal number by a whole
number the answer has the same number of digits
after the decimal point as the original decimal
number.**

Example 12

Work out 8.16×4

$$
\begin{array}{r}
816 \\
\times\ \ 4 \\
\hline
3264 \\
\tiny 2
\end{array}
$$

Remember to show
the carry numbers in
your working out.

8.16
↑↑
There are two digits after
the decimal point, so the
answer has two digits after
the decimal point.

There is more about
multiplication on
page 54.

The answer is 32.64

Exercise 8F

1 Find the cost of:
   (a) 3 books at £4.23 each.
   (b) 4 kg of apples at £0.62 per kg.
   (c) 8 melons at £1.54 each.
   (d) 6 packets of biscuits at £0.64 each.

2 Work out:
   (a) 3.4 × 2   (b) 2.1 × 4   (c) 8.1 × 5
   (d) 3.25 × 3   (e) 14.3 × 8   (f) 5.31 × 6

3 Work out:
   (a) 13.27 × 3   (b) 4.3 × 5   (c) 21.31 × 7
   (d) 7.43 × 5   (e) 6.52 × 4   (f) 16.43 × 8

4 Work out the cost of 4 pairs of socks at £3.42 a pair.

5 Find the total length, in metres, of 6 pieces of wood, each 0.53 metre long.

6 Work out the total length, in metres, of 7 pieces of string, each 0.35 metre long.

7 Find the cost of four CDs at £11.20 each.

8 Calculate the cost of three bottles of lemonade which cost £0.62 each.
   Write your answer in pounds.

9 Work out the cost of five cassettes at £7.50 each.

10 Find the total cost, in pounds, of six magazines priced £1.54 each.

8.5 Dividing decimals by whole numbers

Example 13

Four friends paid £12.48 for a meal. They decide to share the cost equally. How much should they each pay?

$12.48 \div 4$:

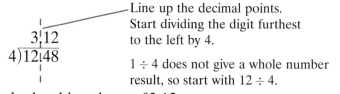

Line up the decimal points.
Start dividing the digit furthest to the left by 4.

$1 \div 4$ does not give a whole number result, so start with $12 \div 4$.

There is more on division on page 57.

The friends should each pay £3.12

■ **When dividing a decimal number by a whole number line up the decimal points and divide as normal.**

Example 14

Work out:

(a) $25.8 \div 6$ **(b)** $47.3 \div 5$

(a)

$$\begin{array}{r} 4.3 \\ 6)\overline{25.^18} \end{array}$$

Line up the decimal point in the answer.
Divide like a normal division sum.

So $25.8 \div 6 = 4.3$

(b)

$$\begin{array}{r} 9.4\,6 \\ 5)\overline{47.^23^30} \end{array}$$

Remember to include the carry numbers.

So $47.3 \div 5 = 9.46$

Exercise 8G

Work these out without a calculator. Show all your working.

1 Find one share if:
  (a) four people share £8.48 equally
  (b) three people share £9.60 equally
  (c) six people share £10.50 equally
  (d) eight people share £33.68 equally.

2   Work out:
   (a) $8.6 \div 2$ **(b)** $36.9 \div 3$ **(c)** $10.5 \div 5$
   (d) $84.8 \div 4$ **(e)** $36.84 \div 6$ **(f)** $64.28 \div 2$

3   Work out:
   (a) $0.672 \div 6$ **(b)** $0.945 \div 7$ **(c)** $1.08 \div 4$
   (d) $5.4 \div 3$ **(e)** $9.027 \div 9$ **(f)** $8.7 \div 5$

4   Sabrina pours 8.4 litres of orange juice into six jugs,
   with the same amount in each jug. How much orange
   juice is in each jug?

5   Four people share the cost of a meal equally. The meal
   costs £18.56. How much does each person pay?

6   22.5 kg of hamster food is packed equally into 9 bags.
   Work out the weight of hamster food in each bag.

8.6 Writing decimal numbers in size order

Sometimes you will need to sort measurements and decimal
numbers in order of size.

- ■   **To sort decimal numbers in order of size:**
  - **first compare the whole numbers**
  - **next compare the tenths**
  - **then compare the hundredths and so on ...**

Example 15

Write these decimal numbers in order of size, starting with
the largest: 0.19, 0.7, 3.1, 0.36, 2.08

First look at the **whole number** part:

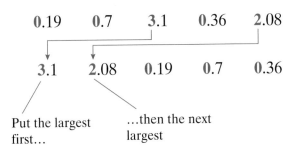

0.19, 0.7 and 0.36 all have 0 units.
Sort them using the tenths digits:

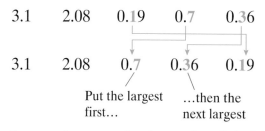

Now the numbers are in size order: 3.1, 2.08, 0.7, 0.36, 0.19

Example 16

Write these decimal numbers in order of size, starting with
the largest: 0.25, 0.31, 0.8, 0.36

The whole number part is the same for each so sort them
using the **tenths**:

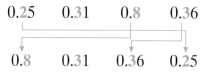

0.31 and 0.36 both have 3 tenths.

Sort them using the **hundredths** digits:

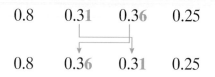

Now the numbers are in size order: 0.8, 0.36, 0.31, 0.25

Exercise 8H

1   Rearrange these decimal numbers in order of size,
    starting with the largest:
    (a) 0.1, 0.8, 0.3 **(b)** 0.5, 0.9, 0.4 **(c)** 0.01, 0.06, 0.08
    (d) 0.07, 0.02, 0.05 **(e)** 0.48, 0.39, 0.62 **(f)** 0.29, 0.4, 0.53
    (g) 0.21, 0.45, 0.6 **(h)** 0.09, 0.4, 0.23 **(i)** 2.08, 0.9, 2.1

2   Put these numbers in order of size, smallest first:
    (a) 0.21, 0.35, 0.41, 0.29 **(b)** 0.62, 0.91, 0.68, 0.95
    (c) 0.23, 0.08, 0.27, 0.06, 0.3 **(d)** 0.27, 0.09, 4.51, 3.29, 3.58
    (e) 3.24, 1.68, 0.21, 0.03, 0.24 **(f)** 3.2, 6.8, 5.4, 3.7, 6.2

8.7 Understanding percentages

The symbol % is read as 'per cent'.
Per cent means 'in every 100'.

9% means '9 in every 100'.
9% is called a percentage.

100% of something is the whole amount.

Example 17

Beth cuts a piece of wood into five equal pieces.
What percentage of the wood is each piece?

The whole piece of wood is 100%.
There are 5 pieces so each piece is $100 \div 5 = 20\%$.

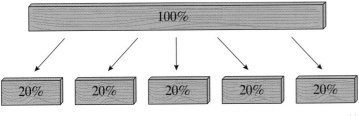

(Check: $20\% + 20\% + 20\% + 20\% + 20\% = 100\%$)

Example 18

What percentage of this shape is shaded?

The whole shape is 100%.
There are 10 squares so each square is:

$$100 \div 10 = 10\%.$$

7 squares shaded, so:

$$7 \times 10\% = 70\% \text{ of the shape is shaded.}$$

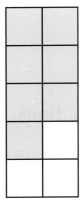

Exercise 8I

1   A rod is cut into ten equal pieces. What percentage of the rod is each piece?

2   A pie is cut into four equal pieces. What percentage of the pie is each piece?

3   In each part work out what percentage the shaded area is of the whole shape.

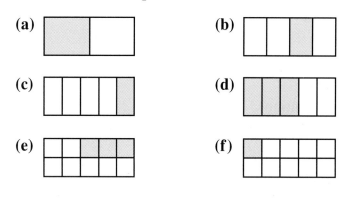

4   What percentage of each shape is shaded?

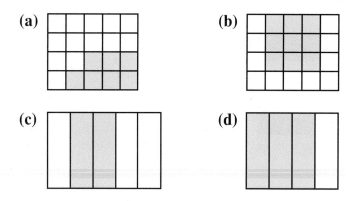

8.8 Fractions, decimals and percentages

You can write a percentage as a fraction.

9% means 9 in every 100. As a fraction this is $\dfrac{9}{100}$ ——— Notice that the denominator is 100

9% and $\dfrac{9}{100}$ represent the same amount.

■   **You can write any percentage as a fraction with the denominator 100.**

For example, $37\% = \dfrac{37}{100}$

These hundred squares show some more fractions and percentages:

$\frac{1}{4}$ shaded

1	2	3	4	5	6	7	8	9	10
11	12	13	14	15	16	17	18	19	20
21	22	23	24	25	26	27	28	29	30
31	32	33	34	35	36	37	38	39	40
41	42	43	44	45	46	47	48	49	50
51	52	53	54	55	56	57	58	59	60
61	62	63	64	65	66	67	68	69	70
71	72	73	74	75	76	77	78	79	80
81	82	83	84	85	86	87	88	89	90
91	92	93	94	95	96	97	98	99	100

25 parts shaded.
25% shaded.

$\frac{1}{2}$ shaded

1	2	3	4	5	6	7	8	9	10
11	12	13	14	15	16	17	18	19	20
21	22	23	24	25	26	27	28	29	30
31	32	33	34	35	36	37	38	39	40
41	42	43	44	45	46	47	48	49	50
51	52	53	54	55	56	57	58	59	60
61	62	63	64	65	66	67	68	69	70
71	72	73	74	75	76	77	78	79	80
81	82	83	84	85	86	87	88	89	90
91	92	93	94	95	96	97	98	99	100

50 parts shaded.
50% shaded.

$\frac{3}{4}$ shaded

1	2	3	4	5	6	7	8	9	10
11	12	13	14	15	16	17	18	19	20
21	22	23	24	25	26	27	28	29	30
31	32	33	34	35	36	37	38	39	40
41	42	43	44	45	46	47	48	49	50
51	52	53	54	55	56	57	58	59	60
61	62	63	64	65	66	67	68	69	70
71	72	73	74	75	76	77	78	79	80
81	82	83	84	85	86	87	88	89	90
91	92	93	94	95	96	97	98	99	100

75 parts shaded.
75% shaded.

Example 19

Write these percentages as fractions in their simplest form:

Remember:
The simplest form means there is no equivalent fraction with smaller numerator and denominator.

(a) 60% **(b)** 2% **(c)** 35%

(a) 60% means $\frac{60}{100}$

$\frac{60}{100} \overset{\div 20}{\underset{\div 20}{=}} \frac{3}{5}$

So 60% = $\frac{3}{5}$

(b) 2% means $\frac{2}{100}$

$\frac{2}{100} \overset{\div 2}{\underset{\div 2}{=}} \frac{1}{50}$

So 2% = $\frac{1}{50}$

(c) 35% means $\frac{35}{100}$

$\frac{35}{100} \overset{\div 5}{\underset{\div 5}{=}} \frac{7}{20}$

So 35% = $\frac{7}{20}$

You can also write a percentage as a decimal:

9% means $\frac{9}{100}$ which means $9 \div 100 = 0.09$

Remember:
To divide by 100 move the digits two places to the right.

■ **To change a percentage to a decimal divide by 100.**
For example: 37% means $37 \div 100 = 0.37$

You can convert any fraction into a decimal by dividing:

$\frac{3}{4} = 3 \div 4 = 0.75$

$\frac{5}{8} = 5 \div 8 = 0.625$

Example 20

Write these percentages as decimals:

(a) 29%   (b) 3%

(a) 29% = 29 ÷ 100 = 0.29   (b) 3% = 3 ÷ 100 = 0.03

■ **You should remember these percentages and their equivalent fractions and decimals:**

Equivalent means they represent the same amount.

$$50\% = \frac{1}{2} = 0.5 \quad 25\% = \frac{1}{4} = 0.25 \quad 75\% = \frac{3}{4} = 0.75$$

$$1\% = \frac{1}{100} = 0.01 \quad 10\% = \frac{1}{10} = 0.1 \quad 20\% = \frac{1}{5} = 0.2$$

Exercise 8J

1 For each hundred square, write down:
- the fraction shaded
- the percentage shaded

(a)

1	2	3	4	5	6	7	8	9	10
11	12	13	14	15	16	17	18	19	20
21	22	23	24	25	26	27	28	29	30
31	32	33	34	35	36	37	38	39	40
41	42	43	44	45	46	47	48	49	50
51	52	53	54	55	56	57	58	59	60
61	62	63	64	65	66	67	68	69	70
71	72	73	74	75	76	77	78	79	80
81	82	83	84	85	86	87	88	89	90
91	92	93	94	95	96	97	98	99	100

(b)

1	2	3	4	5	6	7	8	9	10
11	12	13	14	15	16	17	18	19	20
21	22	23	24	25	26	27	28	29	30
31	32	33	34	35	36	37	38	39	40
41	42	43	44	45	46	47	48	49	50
51	52	53	54	55	56	57	58	59	60
61	62	63	64	65	66	67	68	69	70
71	72	73	74	75	76	77	78	79	80
81	82	83	84	85	86	87	88	89	90
91	92	93	94	95	96	97	98	99	100

(c)

1	2	3	4	5	6	7	8	9	10
11	12	13	14	15	16	17	18	19	20
21	22	23	24	25	26	27	28	29	30
31	32	33	34	35	36	37	38	39	40
41	42	43	44	45	46	47	48	49	50
51	52	53	54	55	56	57	58	59	60
61	62	63	64	65	66	67	68	69	70
71	72	73	74	75	76	77	78	79	80
81	82	83	84	85	86	87	88	89	90
91	92	93	94	95	96	97	98	99	100

2 Write these percentages as fractions in their simplest form.

(a) 20%   (b) 30%   (c) 10%   (d) 60%
(e) 25%   (f) 42%   (g) 35%   (h) 44%
(i) 32%   (j) 75%   (k) 45%   (l) 4%

3 Without a calculator, find:

(a) 50% of £14   (b) 10% of £40   (c) 25% of 12 kg
(d) 1% of 300 g   (e) 75% of 8 m   (f) 20% of £15
(g) 50% of 7 km   (h) 10% of 28 kg   (i) 25% of £6

Hint: Try using an equivalent fraction or decimal to help.

4 Change these percentages to decimals.
   (a) 14%   (b) 37%   (c) 64%   (d) 92%
   (e) 6%   (f) 35%   (g) 24%   (h) 3%
   (i) 27%   (j) 1%   (k) 5%   (l) 63%
   (m) 25%   (n) 17%   (o) 12%   (p) 80%

5 Copy and complete this table of equivalent percentages, fractions and decimals.

Percentage	Fraction	Decimal
60%	$\frac{3}{5}$	0.6
31%		
	$\frac{1}{2}$	
15%		
4%		
		0.19
	$\frac{3}{10}$	
35%		

8.9 Finding a percentage of an amount

Mrs Hayes picks 400 apples from her garden. 15% of the apples she picks are rotten and she must throw them away.

How many apples will she throw away?

■ **To find a percentage of an amount:**
   ● **change the percentage to a decimal**
   ● **multiply the decimal by the amount**

Example 21

Find 15% of 400 apples.

Find the decimal:
$$15\% = \frac{15}{100} = 15 \div 100 = 0.15$$
So:

15%   of   400 apples

⬇   ⬇   ⬇

0.15   ×   400 = 60 apples

Hint:
In percentage questions 'of' means 'multiply'.

Example 22

Find 35% of £250

Find the decimal:
$$35\% = 35 \div 100 = 0.35$$

So:

35%   of   £250

0.35   ×   250 = £87.5

This is a money amount so you must write in the extra 0:

$$35\% \text{ of } £250 = £87.5$$
$$= £87.50$$

Exercise 8K

1   20% of the 600 pupils at Birchtown school go on a school trip. How many pupils go on the trip?

2   Work out:
   (a) 30% of 400 CDs   **(b)** 20% of £400
   (c) 25% of £600   **(d)** 15% of 500 metres
   (e) 15% of 300 children   **(f)** 35% of 700 kilos

3   Work out:
   (a) 10% of £4   **(b)** 20% of £35   **(c)** 50% of £18
   (d) 25% of £28   **(e)** 75% of £32   **(f)** 30% of £40
   (g) 50% of £26   **(h)** 25% of £36   **(i)** 60% of £15

Summary of key points

1   In a decimal number the decimal point separates the whole number from the part that is less than one.

decimal point

63.57

63 is the whole number part

.57 is the part less than one

2 When adding or subtracting with decimals always line up the decimal points.

3 To multiply decimal numbers by 10 move the digits one place to the left.
   To multiply decimal numbers by 100 move the digits two places to the left.
   To multiply decimal numbers by 1000 move the digits three places to the left.

4 To divide decimals by 10 move the digits one place to the right.
   To divide decimal numbers by 100 move the digits two places to the right.
   To divide decimal numbers by 1000 move the digits three places to the right.

5 When you multiply a decimal number by a whole number the answer has the same number of digits after the decimal point as the original decimal number.

6 When dividing a decimal number by a whole number line up the decimal points and divide as normal.

7 To sort decimal numbers in order of size:
   - compare the whole numbers
   - compare the tenths
   - compare the hundredths and so on ...

8 You can write a percentage as a fraction with the denominator 100.
   For example, $37\% = \dfrac{37}{100}$.

9 To change a percentage to a decimal divide by 100.
   For example: 37% means $37 \div 100 = 0.37$.

10 You should remember these percentages and their equivalent fractions and decimals:

   $50\% = \dfrac{1}{2} = 0.5$ $25\% = \dfrac{1}{4} = 0.25$ $75\% = \dfrac{3}{4} = 0.75$

   $1\% = \dfrac{1}{100} = 0.01$ $10\% = \dfrac{1}{10} = 0.5$ $20\% = \dfrac{1}{5} = 0.2$

11 To work out a percentage of an amount:
   - change the percentage to a decimal
   - multiply the decimal by the amount.

9 Shape and measure

9.1 Points, lines and shapes

It is often useful to use letters to name points, lines and shapes:

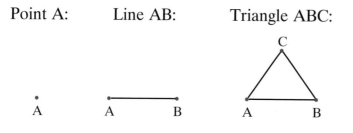

Point A: Line AB: Triangle ABC:

- ■ **You can use capital letters to name points, lines and shapes**

Exercise 9A

1   Name all the lines in these diagrams:

(a)   **(b)**   **(c)**

2   Name all the triangles in these diagrams:

(a)   **(b)**   **(c)**

3   Copy each diagram twice. On each diagram mark:
- A pair of parallel lines. Use letters A, B, C, D.
- A pair of perpendicular lines. Use letters P, Q, R, S.

(a)   **(b)**   **(c)**

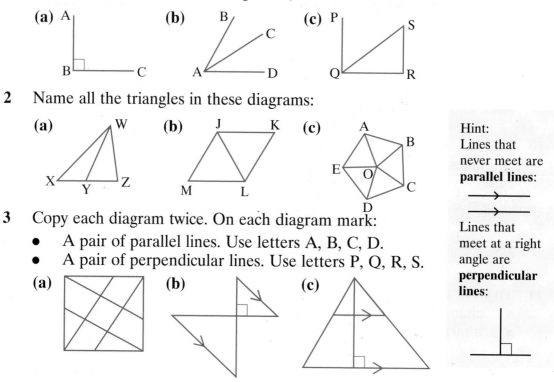

Hint:
Lines that never meet are **parallel lines**:

Lines that meet at a right angle are **perpendicular lines**:

9.2 Quadrilaterals

You should remember these special quadrilaterals:

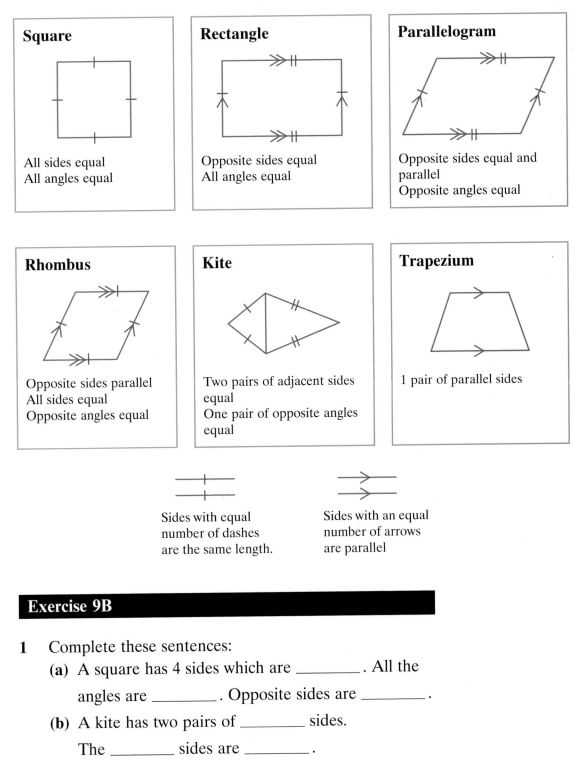

Square

All sides equal
All angles equal

Rectangle

Opposite sides equal
All angles equal

Parallelogram

Opposite sides equal and parallel
Opposite angles equal

Rhombus

Opposite sides parallel
All sides equal
Opposite angles equal

Kite

Two pairs of adjacent sides equal
One pair of opposite angles equal

Trapezium

1 pair of parallel sides

Sides with equal number of dashes are the same length.

Sides with an equal number of arrows are parallel

Exercise 9B

1   Complete these sentences:
   (a) A square has 4 sides which are _____ . All the
   angles are _____ . Opposite sides are _____ .
   (b) A kite has two pairs of _____ sides.
   The _____ sides are _____ .

(c) A _____ has opposite sides equal and all its
angles are right angles.

(d) A parallelogram has opposite sides which
are _____ and _____ .

(e) What is special about a rhombus?

(f) Copy this diagram and use different shading to
show a square, a parallelogram and a trapezium.
What other special quadrilateral is in the diagram?
Name it A, B, C, D.

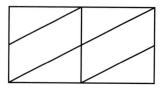

2 There are 11 special quadrilaterals in this diagram.
Name them using letters and their mathematical
names.

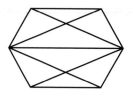

■ **Diagonals of a quadrilateral join opposite corners**

Activity
Use activity sheet 2 to investigate the diagonals of
squares, kites and rhombuses.
Write down your discoveries.

Investigation
Use activity sheet 3 to investigate some properties of
trapeziums.
What do you notice about your results?

9.3 Circles

Different parts of a circle have different names:

■ **The circumference of a circle is its perimeter –
the distance all the way round its edge**

■ **A radius is a straight line from
the centre to the circumference**

■ **A diameter is a straight line from
one point on the circumference to
another that passes through the
centre**

■ **An arc is part of the circumference**
For example, arc AB

Exercise 9C

1   Use letters to name all the arcs, diameters and radii in
the diagram:

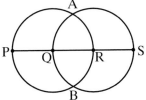

radii is the plural of
radius.
You say 'ray-dee-
eye'.

2   P and Q are the centres of two intersecting circles.

Intersecting means
'cutting across':

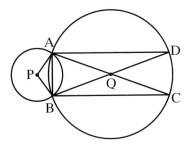

Name all the radii shown.

You can use a pair of compasses to **construct** shapes:

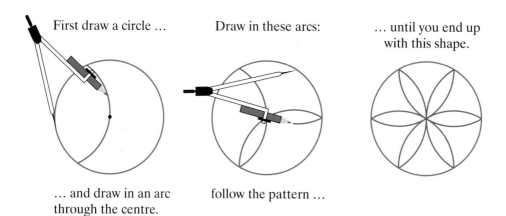

First draw a circle …

… and draw in an arc through the centre.

Draw in these arcs:

follow the pattern …

… until you end up with this shape.

Exercise 9D

Construct these designs using ruler and compasses:

1

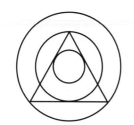

Hint. Draw the two small circles first and then the triangle

2

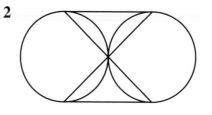

3

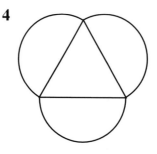

Hint. Draw one straight side and its arcs first

4

9.4 Solid shapes

You should be able to recognize these common solids:

Name:	Shape:		Properties:
Cuboid		A cardboard box is a cuboid	Six rectangular faces
Cube		Regular dice are cubes	Six square faces
Square-based pyramid		The great pyramids in Egypt	Base is square It has 4 triangular sides
Cone		Like a party hat	A special pyramid with a circular base
Prism		These boxes are prisms	Any shape that has a constant cross-section is a prism
Cylinder		These tins are all cylinders	A special prism that has a circular cross-section
Sphere		The shape of a snooker ball	The shape of a ball
Hemisphere		An igloo is a hemisphere	Half of a sphere

Exercise 9E

1 What mathematical name best describes the shape of these tents?

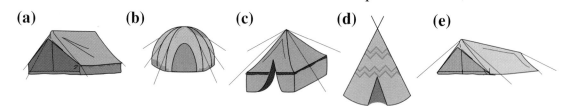

(a)   (b)   (c)   (d)   (e)

2 Name the solids that make up these shapes:

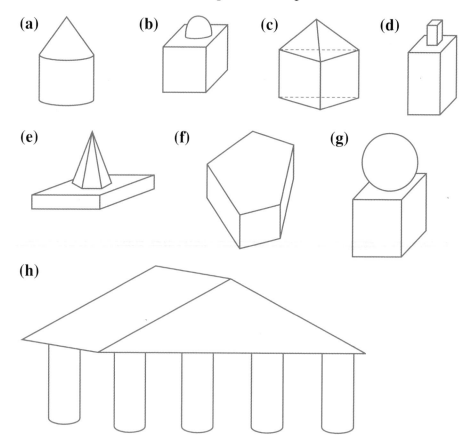

(a)   (b)   (c)   (d)

(e)   (f)   (g)

(h)

9.5 Drawing solid shapes

This section shows you how to draw shapes on paper so that they look solid.

There are two things to remember:

- Vertical lines are always drawn vertically
- Parallel lines are always drawn parallel

To draw a cube:

Draw a square as the
front ...

... draw in the edges from
the three corners

... and join the ends up

Exercise 9F

1 Experiment with drawing cubes. Try making them face
in different directions and make them different sizes.

2 Draw 2 cubes joined together:
- side by side
- on top of each other
- one behind the other

3 Draw three cubes in the shape of an L.

4 Use activity sheet 4 to draw 3D letters. L has been
done for you. See if you can draw I, T, F, E and H.

5 Copy these shapes into your book. Try tracing them
first to work out how to draw them.

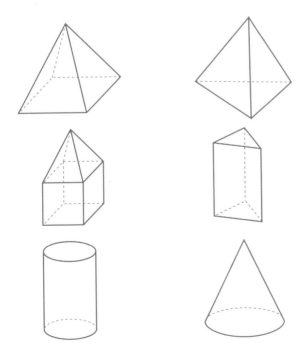

Hint:
Dotted lines show
where hidden edges
are.

9.6 Nets

You can make models of the common solids from a sheet of cardboard.

■ **A shape that folds together to make a solid is called a net of the solid.**

Imagine a cube being unfolded:

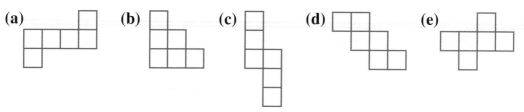

The final shape is the net of the cube.

Exercise 9G

1 Which of these could be the net of a cube?

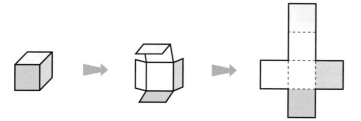

(a)　　　(b)　　　(c)　　　(d)　　　(e)

2 Use activity sheet 5 to make the solids from these nets.

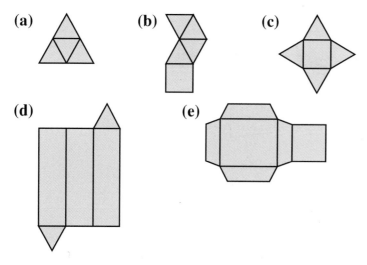

(a)　　　(b)　　　(c)

(d)　　　(e)

9.7 Measure

You should be used to using centimetres, metres and kilometres. For very small lengths you need to use **millimetres** (mm).

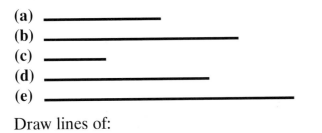

1 mm is about the width of a pencil lead.

■ **10 millimetres (mm) = 1 centimetre (cm)**
  1 millimetre (mm) = $\frac{1}{10}$ cm

Exercise 9H

1 Measure these lines to the nearest mm.

(a) ————————

(b) ————————————

(c) ————

(d) —————————

(e) ——————————————

2 Draw lines of:

(a) 25 mm   (b) 75 mm   (c) 42 mm

Example 1

Write 15 mm in cm and 25 cm in mm.

$$15\,\text{mm} = 15 \div 10$$
$$= 1.5\,\text{cm}$$
$$25\,\text{cm} = 25 \times 10$$
$$= 250\,\text{mm}$$

To change mm to cm you divide by 10. To change cm to mm you multiply by 10.

Exercise 9I

1 Write in cm:

(a) 30 mm   (b) 70 mm   (c) 110 mm   (d) 250 mm
(e) 125 mm   (f) 215 mm   (g) 85 mm   (h) 105 mm
(i) 3050 mm (j) 3005 mm

2 Write in mm:

(a) 1 cm   (b) 3 cm   (c) 5 cm   (d) 2.5 cm
(e) 3.5 cm   (f) 12.5 cm   (g) 10.5 cm   (h) 9.6 cm
(i) 3.7 cm   (j) 8.9 cm

9.8 Capacity

■ **The capacity of a hollow object measures the space inside it**

The capacity of this test tube is 10 millilitres (10 ml)

This petrol can has a capacity of 10 litres (10 *l*)

There are 1000 millilitres in a litre:

1 litre (*l*) = 1000 millilitres (ml)

Example 2

A glass holds 250 ml. How many glasses can be filled from a 3 litre bottle?

3 litres = 3000 millilitres

So, number of glasses filled = 3000 ÷ 250 = 12

Answer 12 glasses.

Exercise 9J

1 Write in millilitres:

  (a) 3 *l*   **(b)** 5 *l*   **(c)** 10 *l*   **(d)** 1.5 *l*
  (e) 3.5 *l*   **(f)** $4\frac{1}{2}$ *l*   **(g)** 0.5 *l*   **(h)** $10\frac{1}{2}$ *l*

To change ml to *l* you divide by 1000. To change *l* to ml you multiply by 1000.

2 Write in litres:

  (a) 4000 ml   **(b)** 8000 ml
  (c) 10 000 ml   **(d)** 3500 ml
  (e) 500 ml   **(f)** 10 500 ml
  (g) 1200 ml   **(h)** 5700 ml
  (i) 9200 ml   **(j)** 700 ml

3 Each of John's soup bowls holds 400 ml.
  How many bowls can he fill from a 2 litre pan of soup.

4   A glass holds 250 ml.
How many glasses can be filled from a 2 litre bottle?

5   A tank holds 50 litres.
Heather fills the tank using a jug that holds 200 ml.
How many jugfuls must she put in to fill the tank?

9.9 Imperial measure

The measurements you have used so far are all metric.
You should also know these common imperial measures:

metric:	**imperial:**
8 kilometres	= 5 miles
30 centimetres	= 1 foot
1 litre	= 1.75 pints

Example 3

Mr Khalid drives 160 km to visit his parents.
How far is that in miles?

   8 kilometres = 5 miles

Divide 160 by 8:

   $160 \div 8 = 20$

There are 20 lots of 8 km which is the same as 20 lots of 5 miles:

   $20 \times 5 = 100$ miles

So there are 100 miles in 160 km.

Example 4

How many feet are there in 1.8 metres?

   30 cm = 1 foot

1.8 metres is 180 centimetres so divide 180 by 30:

   $180 \div 30 = 6$

There are 6 lots of 30 cm which is the same as 6 lots of 1 foot

   $6 \times 1 = 6$ feet

So there are 6 feet in 1.8 m.

Exercise 9K

1 Change these distances into miles:

(a) 40 km   (b) 24 km   (c) 16 km   (d) 400 km

(e) 208 km   (f) 152 km   (g) 48 km   (h) 20 km

> Remember:
> 8 km = 5 miles
> 30 cm = 1 foot
> 1 litre = 17.5 pints

2 Change these into feet:

(a) 60 cm   (b) 120 cm   (c) 300 cm   (d) 660 cm

(e) 105 cm   (f) 1080 cm   (g) 210 cm   (h) 15 cm

3 Change these litre measurements into pints:

(a) 4 litres   (b) 10 *l*   (c) 2 *l*   (d) 12 *l*   (e) 5.5 *l*

Make up some questions, with answers, for changing miles into kilometres, feet into centimetres and pints into litres.

9.10 Time

You should know how to use both 12-hour and 24-hour clock times:

For times between midnight and midday:

12-hour clock: 24-hour clock:

04:10

You write the time followed by **am**:
4:10 am

You write the hours the same:
04:10

> 24-hour clock times always have four digits so you must put an extra zero at the start.

For times between midday and midnight:

12-hour clock: 24-hour clock:

16:10

You write the time followed by **pm**:
4:10 pm

You add 12 to the hours digit:
16:10

> For 24-hour clock times between midnight and 1 am you write the hours as 00.
>
> You write 12:23 am as 00:23

Example 5

It is 8:55 am.
What time will it be in 15 minutes?

There are 60 minutes in an hour so it will be 9 am
in 5 minutes. This leaves another 10 minutes so the answer
must be 9:10 am.

Example 6

How long is it between 11:45 and 13:15?
Break the time down like this:

$$11:45 \rightarrow 12:00 = 15 \text{ minutes}$$
$$12:00 \rightarrow 13:00 = 1 \text{ hour}$$
$$13:00 \rightarrow 13:15 = 15 \text{ minutes}$$

So in total it is 1 hour + 15 minutes + 15 minutes
= 1 hour 30 minutes.

Exercise 9L

1   Write these as 24-hour clock times:
   (a) 7:45 am   **(b)** 3:26 pm   **(c)** 11:50 pm
   (d) 12:27 am   **(e)** 5:30 pm   **(f)** 1:16 am

> Remember:
> 24-hour clock times
> must always have
> four digits.

2   Write these as 12-hour clock times:
   (a) 09:30   **(b)** 11:20   **(c)** 20:05
   (d) 12:19   **(e)** 00:56   **(f)** 15:40

3   For **(a)** to **(f)** write down what the time will be after:
   * 15 minutes
   * 40 minutes
   * 1 hour 20 minutes

   Give your answer as a 12-hour and a 24-hour clock
   time.
   (a) 8:45 am   **(b)** 09:15   **(c)** 10:50
   (d) 03:52   **(e)** 6:48 pm   **(f)** 00:30

4   How long is it between:
 (a) 7:15 am and 7:37 am   (b) 08:50 and 09:15
 (c) 11:35 am and 12:45 am (d) 17:40 and 19:30
 (e) 2:50 pm and 5:10 pm   (f) 1:15 pm and 6:45 pm
 (g) 15:22 and 16:08   (h) 3:35 am and 8:30 am
 (i) 11:54 pm and 1:05 am   (j) 22:45 and 00:32

Summary of key points

1   You can use capital letters to name points, lines and shapes.

2   The diagonals of a quadrilateral join opposite corners.

3   The circumference of a circle is its perimeter – the distance all the way round its edge.

4   The radius is the distance from the centre to the circumference.

5   The diameter is a straight line across a circle that passes through the centre

6   An arc is part of the circumference.

7   A shape that you can fold to make a solid is called a net of the solid.

8   10 millimetres (mm) = 1 centimetre (cm)
    1 millimetre (mm) = $\frac{1}{10}$ cm

9   The capacity of a hollow object measures the space inside it.
    1 litre (*l*)   = 1000 millilitres (ml)

10 You should also know the common imperial measures.

    8 kilometres   = 5 miles
    30 centimetres = 1 foot
    1 litre   = 1.75 pints

10 Positive and negative numbers

10.1 Using temperatures

Temperatures are often measured in degrees Celsius, written °C for short.

Water freezes when it has a temperature of zero degrees Celsius.

0°C is called the freezing point of water.

A person's normal temperature is 37° Celsius above zero written as +37°C or 37°C.

The temperature in this freezer is 20° Celsius below zero.

You write −20°C.

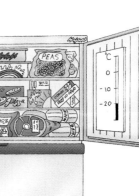

- ■ **Positive numbers are greater than zero. They are sometimes written with a plus sign. For example: +2 or 2**

- ■ **Negative numbers are less than zero. They are written with a minus sign. For example: −5**

Example 1

What temperature does the thermometer show?
Write your answer:
(a) in words   (b) in figures.

The temperature is four degrees below zero so it is written:

(a) negative four degrees Celsius
    You will often hear this called 'minus four degrees'.
(b) −4°C.

Example 2

Show these temperatures on a thermometer:

(a) $+2°C$ **(b)** $-1°C$.

(a) The temperature $+2°C$ means two degrees Celsius above zero. This is what it looks like on the thermometer:

(b) The temperature $-1°C$ means one degree Celsius below zero. This is what it looks like on the thermometer:

Exercise 10A

1 Write down the temperature each thermometer shows in words and in figures.

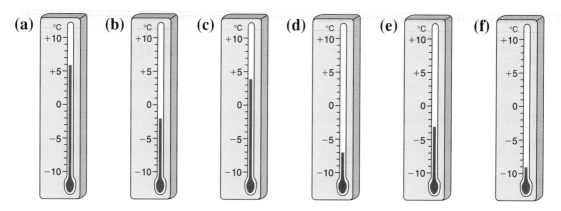

(a)   **(b)**   **(c)**   **(d)**   **(e)**   **(f)**

2 Draw these temperatures on the thermometers on activity sheet 6. The first one has been done for you.

(a) $+8°C$	**(b)** $-3°C$	**(c)** $-6°C$
(d) $-7°C$	**(e)** $-1°C$	**(f)** $-4°C$
(g) $+9°C$	**(h)** $+7°C$	**(i)** $-2°C$
(j) $-11°C$	**(k)** $+3°C$	**(l)** $-8°C$
(m) $+1°C$	**(n)** $-9°C$	**(o)** $+5°C$
(p) $-10°C$	**(q)** $4°C$	**(r)** $-5°C$
(s) $+2°C$	**(t)** $6°C$	

10.2 Writing temperatures in order of size

Sometimes you need to find the highest and lowest values from a list of temperatures or write the list in order of size.

On this weather map the numbers are temperatures in degrees Celsius.

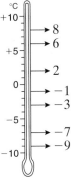

If a temperature is written '8°C' it means plus eight degrees Celsius or +8°C.

Example 3

From the weather map write down:
(a) the highest temperature in °C,
(b) the lowest temperature in °C,
(c) all the temperatures in order of size, starting with the highest.

(a) The highest temperature is 8°C.
(b) The lowest temperature is −9°C.
(c) Draw a diagram like a thermometer with a scale going from −10°C to 10°C.
    Write each temperature from the weather map at the correct place on the thermometer scale.
    Write down the temperatures in order, starting from the top of the thermometer.
    8°C, 6°C, 2°C, −1°C, −3°C, −7°C, −9°C.

Notice that −9° is below all the others.

Example 4

From the temperatures −1°C, +5°C, −13°C, +2°C, −4°C, −8°C, write down
(a) the highest temperature,
(b) the lowest temperature,
(c) all the temperatures in order of size, starting with the lowest.

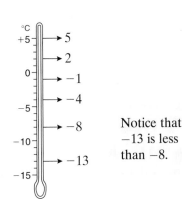

Look at this vertical thermometer.

(a) The highest temperature is highest on the scale, +5°C.
(b) The lowest temperature is lowest on the scale, −13°C.
(c) In order of size the temperatures are:
    −13°C, −8°C, −4°C, −1°C, +2°C, +5°C.

Notice that −13 is less than −8.

Exercise 10B

On the weather maps in questions **1** and **2**, the
numbers show temperatures in degrees Celsius.

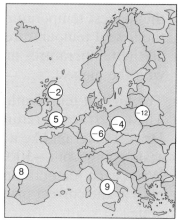

1   From the weather map write down:
   (a) the hottest place,
   (b) the coldest place,
   (c) all the temperatures in order of size,
      starting with the highest.

2   Look at the weather map and write down:
   (a) the highest temperature,
   (b) the lowest temperature.
   (c) all the temperatures in
      order of size, starting with
      the lowest.

3   Write down the higher of the two temperatures:
   (a) 1°C   and 5°C   **(b)** −9°C and 2°C
   (c) −1°C and 0°C   **(d)** −2°C and 3°C
   (e) −5°C and −3°C   **(f)** −2°C and −6°C

4   Write down the lower of the two temperatures:
   (a) 3°C   and 7°C   **(b)** 0°C   and −3°C
   (c) −4°C and 2°C   **(d)** −5°C and −4°C
   (e) −6°C and −9°C   **(f)** −5°C and −8°C

5   Write down the highest temperature in each list:
   (a) +1°C, −4°C, +2°C, −8°C, +8°C, −7°C.
   (b) 0°C, +2°C, −5°C, −9°C, −2°C, +3°C.
   (c) −4°C, −7°C, −2°C, −6°C, −10°C, −5°C.
   (d) −4°C, −8°C, −7°C, −3°C, −9°C, −2°C.

6   Write the lowest temperature in each list:
   (a) +4°C, −1°C, +5°C, −5°C, +10°C, −4°C.
   (b) +3°C, +5°C, −2°C, −6°C, −1°C, +6°C.
   (c) +9°C, −6°C, +4°C, −3°C, +6°C, −2°C.
   (d) −1°C, −2°C, −7°C, −6°C, 2°C, −5°C.

7 Write these temperatures in order of size, starting with the highest.

(a) −4°C, −1°C, 3°C, −3°C, −7°C, 10°C.
(b) 3°C, −4°C, 1°C, −8°C, −7°C, −1°C.
(c) −4°C, 1°C, −2°C, −7°C, −6°C, −1°C.
(d) −8°C, −3°C, −6°C, −1°C, 2°C, −10°C.

8 Write these temperatures in order of size, starting with the lowest.

(a) 4°C, −1°C, −5°C, −9°C, 1°C, −4°C.
(b) −6°C, −10°C, 5°C, −3°C, 2°C, −2°C.
(c) −1°C, −6°C, 1°C, −8°C, 4°C, −9°C.
(d) −5°C, 1°C, −11°C, −8°C, −4°C, 2°C.

10.3 Moving between positive and negative temperatures

You can use this picture of a thermometer to answer questions involving changes in temperature.

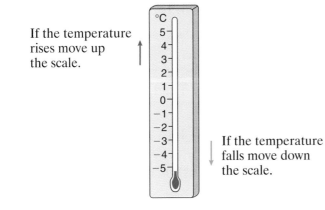

If the temperature rises move up the scale.

If the temperature falls move down the scale.

Example 5

The temperature in Sheffield at midnight was −2°C. By noon the following day the temperature had gone up to 5°C. Work out the rise in the temperature.

Start at the −2°C mark. To get to the 5°C mark you go up 7 degrees.

The rise in the temperature was 7°C.

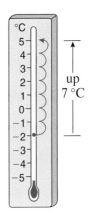

up
7 °C

Example 6

The temperature in Princetown at midnight was $-4°$C.
By noon the following day the temperature had gone up
by $6°$C. Work out the temperature in Princetown at noon.

Start at the $-4°$C mark and go up six degrees.
You end up at $2°$C.

The temperature in Princetown at noon was $2°$C.

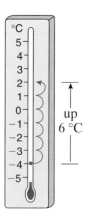

Exercise 10C

1 The temperature in Dunstable at midnight was $-3°$C.
By noon the next day the temperature had gone up to
$5°$C. Work out the rise in the temperature.

2 The temperature in Reading at noon was $4°$C. By 8 pm
the same day the temperature had gone down to $-2°$C.
Work out the drop in the temperature.

3 The temperature in Talgarth at midnight was $-5°$C. By
noon the next day the temperature had gone up by
eight degrees. Work out the temperature in Talgarth at
noon.

4 The temperature in Leicester at noon was $-1°$C. By
midnight the temperature had gone down by seven
degrees. What was the temperature in Leicester at
midnight?

Hint: you
can use this
thermometer
to help you.

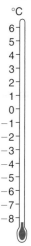

Copy and complete the tables for questions **5** and **6**.

5

Town	Temperature at midnight	Temperature at noon the next day	Rise in temperature
(a)	$-2°$C	$6°$C	
(b)	$-1°$C	$4°$C	
(c)	$-4°$C	$0°$C	
(d)	$-1°$C		$7°$C
(e)	$-3°$C		$5°$C
(f)	$-5°$C		$3°$C

6

Town	Temperature at noon	Temperature at 2 am the next day	Fall in temperature
(a)	4°C	0°C	
(b)	3°C	−4°C	
(c)	−3°C	−8°C	
(d)	−3°C		6°C
(e)	0°C		3°C
(f)	−5°C		2°C

10.4 Using a vertical number line

A vertical number line can help you solve problems
involving positive and negative numbers.

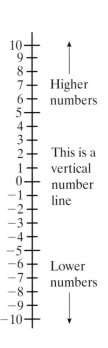

■ **You can use a vertical number line to:**
  ● **find the highest and lowest values in a set of values**
  ● **write a list of values in order of size**
  ● **answer questions involving changes in values.**

Example 7

(a) Start at number −3 and end at 4. How many have you gone up?
(b) Start at −2 and end at −6. How many have you gone down?

(a) You have gone up 7.

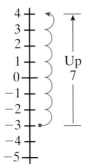

(b) You have gone down 4.

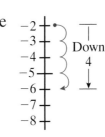

Example 8

Which number is greater, −4 or −9?

Find the numbers −4 and −9 on a vertical number line, −4 is higher up than −9. So −4 is greater than −9.

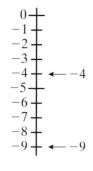

Example 9

Write down all the whole numbers between −6 and 3.

Using a vertical number line write down all the numbers that are above −6 and below 3.
The numbers are −5, −4, −3, −2, −1, 0, 1, 2.

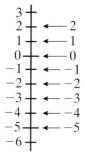

Example 10

Rowan chooses an even number that is greater than −6 and less than −2. What number did Rowan choose?

Using a vertical number line the numbers that are greater than −6 and less than −2 are −5, −4 and −3. Only −4 is an even number.
So Rowan must have chosen −4.

Exercise 10D

Use a vertical number line to help you with these questions.

1   Write down the highest number in each list:
   (a) +2, −3, +5, −7, −2.
   (b) −3, 0, +1, −6, +4.

2   Write down the lowest number in each list:
   (a) +1, −2, 0, −5, +3.
   (b) −4, +5, −1, +2, −2.

3 Write these numbers in order of size, starting with the lowest:
  (a) 5, −2, −4, −8, 2, −3.
  (b) 0, −5, 2, −7, 5, −8.

4 Start at number −5 and end at 4. How many have you gone up?

5 Start at number −9 and end at −3. How many have you gone up?

6 Start at number 3 and end at −7. How many have you gone down?

7 Start at number −1 and end at −8. How many have you gone down?

8 Sharon chooses two counters at a time from a bag of numbered counters. These are the numbers on them each time. Which is the higher number each time?
  (a) −3, +2   **(b)** +1, −4   **(c)** −2, −6
  (d) −7, 3   **(e)** 1, −6   **(f)** −5, −2
  (g) −7, −9   **(h)** −2, −8.

9 Javed chooses two counters at a time from a bag of numbered counters. These are the numbers on them each time. Which is the lower number each time?
  (a) −5, +3   **(b)** −2, −1   **(c)** −1, 8   **(d)** 5, −7
  (e) −6, −2   **(f)** −6, +5   **(g)** −4, −5   **(h)** −8, −4.

10 Write down all the whole numbers between:
  (a) −4 and 3   **(b)** −5 and 2   **(c)** −7 and −1
  (d) −3 and 4   **(e)** −6 and 1   **(f)** −9 and −3
  (g) −2 and −8   **(h)** −4 and −9.

11 Kevin chooses an even number that is greater than −8 and less than −4. What is the number Kevin chooses?

12 Sean chooses a number that is less than −4, greater than −9 and is a multiple of 3. What is the number Sean chooses?

13 Tracey chooses an odd number that is greater than −5 and less than −1. What is the number Tracey chooses?

10.5 Counting on or back

You need to be able to count up and down from a positive or negative number.

■ **You can use a vertical number line marked with positive and negative numbers to count on or back.**

Example 11

Use a vertical number line to find the number that is:

(a) 5 more than 4   (b) 3 more than −7
(c) 7 less than 2   (d) 4 less than −5.

(a) If you start at 4 and go up 5 you end at 9.

So 5 more than 4 is 9.

(b) If you start at −7 and go up 3 you end at −4.

So 3 more than −7 is −4.

(c) If you start at 2 and go down 7 you end at −5.

So 7 less than 2 is −5.

(d) If you start at −5 and go down 4 you end at −9.

So 4 less than −5 is −9.

Example 12

(a) Start at 4 and go up 3. What number do you end at?
(b) Start at −4 and go up 3. What number do you end at?
(c) Start at 4 and go down 3. What number do you end at?
(d) Start at −4 and go down 3. What number do you end at?

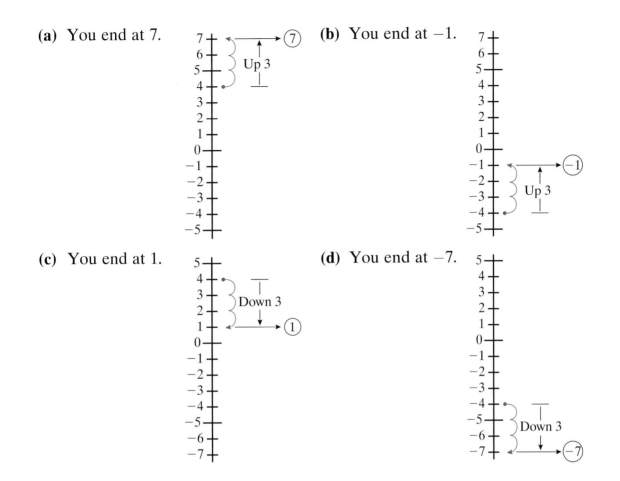

(a) You end at 7.

(b) You end at −1.

(c) You end at 1.

(d) You end at −7.

Exercise 10E

Use a vertical number line to help you with these questions.

1 What number do you get if you:

(a) start at −7 and go up 3.
(b) start at −4 and go up 3.
(c) start at −4 and go up 6.
(d) start at 2 and go up 7.
(e) start at −3 and go up 3.
(f) start at −6 and go up 7.

2 What number do you get if you:

(a) start at −7 and go down 3.
(b) start at −4 and go down 3.
(c) start at −4 and go down 6.
(d) start at 2 and go down 7.
(e) start at −3 and go down 3.
(f) start at −6 and go down 7.

3   Use a vertical number line to find the number that is:

    (a) 7 more than 2   **(b)** 5 more than -2

    (c) 8 less than 7   **(d)** 3 less than -1

    (e) 9 more than -6 **(f)** 4 less than 0

    (g) 12 less than 6   **(h)** 3 less than -4

    (i) 5 more than -5 **(j)** 2 more than -3

4   Nicki and David use a number line to play a game.
Nicki starts at -8 and moves up 2 at a time.
David starts at -8 and moves up 3 at a time.

Write down the numbers less than 30 that they each land on.

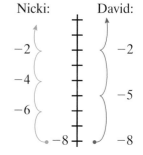

10.6 Working with positive and negative numbers

You can also use a number line to work out the answers to questions like this:

Example 13

Find the value of   **(a)** $-3 + 4$ **(b)** $3 - 7$.

(a) $-3 + 4$

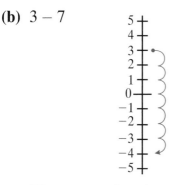

This means start at -3 and then **add** 4.
You start at -3 and **count up** 4.

The answer is 1.

(b) $3 - 7$

This means start at 3 and then **take away** 7.
You start at 3 and **count down** 7.

The answer is -4.

Exercise 10F

Use a vertical number line to answer these questions.

1
  (a) $5 - 3$ **(b)** $4 - 7$ **(c)** $3 - 8$
  (d) $2 - 9$ **(e)** $-4 + 3$ **(f)** $-2 + 7$
  (g) $-3 + 6$ **(h)** $-2 - 4$ **(i)** $-5 - 4$
  (j) $-9 + 3$ **(k)** $3 - 5$ **(l)** $-2 + 6$

2
  (a) $-4 + 2$ **(b)** $3 - 6$ **(c)** $-3 + 5$
  (d) $4 - 2$ **(e)** $-9 + 4$ **(f)** $-2 - 3$
  (g) $1 + 6$ **(h)** $-7 + 3$ **(i)** $4 - 7$
  (j) $-3 - 5$ **(k)** $5 - 8$ **(l)** $-15 + 3$

3   This table can be used to add the first number (blue)
to the second number (pink).

+	-5	-4	-3	-2	-1	0	1	2	3	4	5
1							2			5	
2	-3										
3											
4			1						7		
5											
6						6					
7											
8				6							
9								11			
10											15

Some results have been filled in for you.
For example,

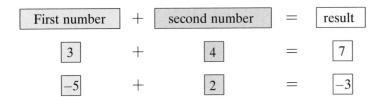

10 — 9 — 8 — 7 — 6 — 5 — 4 — 3 — 2 — 1 — 0 — −1 — −2 — −3 — −4 — −5 — −6 — −7 — −8 — −9 — −10

- On activity sheet 7, complete the shaded section of the square using the rule:

| First number | + | second number | = | result |

- Look for patterns in the table.
  Use your patterns to complete every square in the table.
- Use your completed table to work out

(a) $3+7$ **(b)** $-3+7$ **(c)** $5+6$ **(d)** $-5+6$ **(e)** $-2+3$ **(f)** $-4+1$
(g) $-5+3$ **(h)** $-1+9$ **(i)** $-3+1$ **(j)** $-4+3$ **(k)** $-4+8$ **(l)** $-3+9$

4 Write down all the numbers that are greater than -7, less than 5 and are odd.

5 Write down all the numbers that are less than 7, greater than -5 and are even.

6 Write down all the numbers that are less than 8, greater than -5 and are multiples of 3.

7 Jo starts at -18 and goes up 2 each time.
Write down in order all the numbers she gets that are smaller than 40.
Dean starts at -18 and goes up 3 each time.
Write down in order all the numbers he gets that are smaller than 40.
What do you notice about the numbers that Jo gets and the numbers that Dean gets?

8 Tom starts at 50 and goes down 6 each time.
Write down in order all the numbers he gets that are bigger than -50.
Lisa starts at 50 and goes down 5 each time.
Write down in order all the numbers she gets that are bigger than -50.
Compare the numbers that Tom gets with the numbers that Lisa gets.

10.7 Using a horizontal number line

Sometimes it is useful to mark positive and negative numbers on a horizontal number line.

Here is an example of a horizontal scale on a thermometer

■ **You can use a horizontal number line to answer questions about positive and negative numbers. The smallest number is always on the left.**

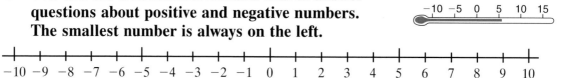

Example 14

Use a horizontal number line to find the number that is
(a) 2 more than 3   **(b)** 4 more than −6
(c) 6 less than 4   **(d)** 3 less than −5

(a) If you have 2 more, the number gets bigger so you
    move to the right. Start at 3 and move two to the right.
    The result is 5.

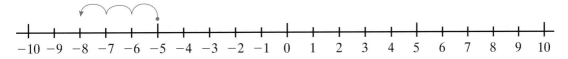

-10 −9 −8 −7 −6 −5 −4 −3 −2 −1 0 1 2 3 4 5 6 7 8 9 10

(b) If you have 4 more, the number gets bigger so you
    move to the right. Start at −6 and move four to the
    right. The result is −2.

-10 −9 −8 −7 −6 −5 −4 −3 −2 −1 0 1 2 3 4 5 6 7 8 9 10

(c) If you have 6 less, the number gets smaller so you
    move to the left. Start at 4 and move six to the left. The
    result is −2.

-10 −9 −8 −7 −6 −5 −4 −3 −2 −1 0 1 2 3 4 5 6 7 8 9 10

(d) If you have 3 less, the number gets smaller so you
    move to the left. Start at −5 and move three to the left.
    The result is −8.

-10 −9 −8 −7 −6 −5 −4 −3 −2 −1 0 1 2 3 4 5 6 7 8 9 10

Example 15

Work out the result of these:
(a) Start at −5 and go up 2.   **(b)** Start at 2 and go down 6.

(a)

−6 −5 −4 −3 −2 −1 0

If you go **up** 2 the number gets
bigger, so you move 2 gaps **to the
right**.
The result is −3.

(b)

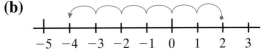

−5 −4 −3 −2 −1 0 1 2 3

If you go **down** 6 the number gets
smaller, so you move 6 gaps **to the
left**.
The result is −4.

Example 16

Find the value of
(a) $2+7$ **(b)** $-2+7$ **(c)** $2-7$ **(d)** $-2-7$.

(a) $2+7$ means start at 2 and move 7 to the right. So
$2+7=9$.

$$
\begin{array}{c|ccccccccccccccccccccc}
 & \text{\small$-10$} & \text{\small$-9$} & \text{\small$-8$} & \text{\small$-7$} & \text{\small$-6$} & \text{\small$-5$} & \text{\small$-4$} & \text{\small$-3$} & \text{\small$-2$} & \text{\small$-1$} & 0 & 1 & 2 & 3 & 4 & 5 & 6 & 7 & 8 & 9 & 10
\end{array}
$$

(b) $-2+7$ means start at -2 and move 7 to the right. So
$-2+7=5$.

$$
\begin{array}{c|ccccccccccccccccccccc}
 & -10 & -9 & -8 & -7 & -6 & -5 & -4 & -3 & -2 & -1 & 0 & 1 & 2 & 3 & 4 & 5 & 6 & 7 & 8 & 9 & 10
\end{array}
$$

(c) $2-7$ means start at 2 and move 7 to the left. So
$2-7=-5$.

$$
\begin{array}{c|ccccccccccccccccccccc}
 & -10 & -9 & -8 & -7 & -6 & -5 & -4 & -3 & -2 & -1 & 0 & 1 & 2 & 3 & 4 & 5 & 6 & 7 & 8 & 9 & 10
\end{array}
$$

(d) $-2-7$ means start at -2 and move 7 to the left. So
$-2-7=-9$.

$$
\begin{array}{c|ccccccccccccccccccccc}
 & -10 & -9 & -8 & -7 & -6 & -5 & -4 & -3 & -2 & -1 & 0 & 1 & 2 & 3 & 4 & 5 & 6 & 7 & 8 & 9 & 10
\end{array}
$$

Exercise 10G

1   Find the number that is:
   (a) 6 more than 3   **(b)** 7 more than -2 **(c)** 4 less than -5
   (d) 4 less than -2 **(e)** 8 more than -5 **(f)** 3 less than 0
   (g) 6 more than -3 **(h)** 5 more than -2 **(i)** 5 more than -5
   (j) 9 more than -5 **(k)** 3 more than -7 **(l)** 5 more than -4.

2   What number is:
   (a) 2 more than -5 **(b)** 3 less than -7 **(c)** 7 less than -3
   (d) 8 less than 2   **(e)** 2 less than -4 **(f)** 5 more than 3
   (g) 4 more than -1 **(h)** 6 more than -4 **(i)** 8 more than -3
   (j) 3 less than -3 **(k)** 3 more than -2 **(l)** 2 more than -9

3 Work out the result of these:
   (a) Start at -2 and go up 5
   (b) Start at -5 and go up 3
   (c) Start at -8 and go up 4
   (d) Start at -3 and go up 9
   (e) Start at 4 and go down 6
   (f) Start at -3 and go down 1
   (g) Start at -2 and go down 7
   (h) Start at 2 and go down 6
   (i) Start at -5 and go up 4
   (j) Start at -7 and go down 2
   (k) Start at -10 and go up 7
   (l) Start at -6 and go down 4

4 Find the value of:
   (a) $8 - 3$ **(b)** $3 - 4$ **(c)** $4 - 7$ **(d)** $3 - 9$
   (e) $-5 + 3$ **(f)** $-3 + 7$ **(g)** $-2 + 5$ **(h)** $-3 - 7$
   (i) $-6 - 3$ **(j)** $-8 + 5$ **(k)** $2 - 6$ **(l)** $-9 + 5$

5 Find the value of:
   (a) $7 - 2$ **(b)** $3 - 7$ **(c)** $2 - 8$ **(d)** $5 - 7$
   (e) $-5 + 2$ **(f)** $-4 + 9$ **(g)** $-2 + 6$ **(h)** $-3 - 6$
   (i) $-5 - 3$ **(j)** $-10 + 4$ **(k)** $1 - 7$ **(l)** $-5 + 6$

10.8 Ordering positive and negative numbers

There are other tasks where a horizontal number line will help.

■ **You can use a horizontal number line to:**
   ● **write positive and negative numbers in order**
   ● **continue number patterns**

Example 17

Write down these numbers in order of size, starting with the smallest:
   $4, 1, -4, -9, -1, 0, -3, -7.$

The order is $-9, -7, -4, -3, -1, 0, 1, 4.$

Example 18

Write down all the even numbers that are bigger than -10 and smaller than 3.

Notice that -10 and 3 are not included in the answers.

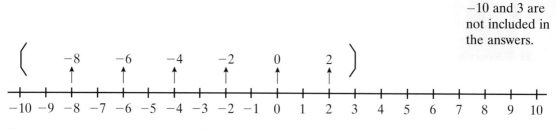

Using a horizontal number line the numbers are $-8, -6, -4, -2, 0$ and 2.

Example 19

Work out the two missing numbers in each number pattern:

(a) $9, 7, 5, 3, \ldots, \ldots, -3.$ **(b)** $-13, -10, -7, -4, \ldots, \ldots, 5.$

(a) The numbers get smaller by 2 each time. The missing numbers are 1 and -1.

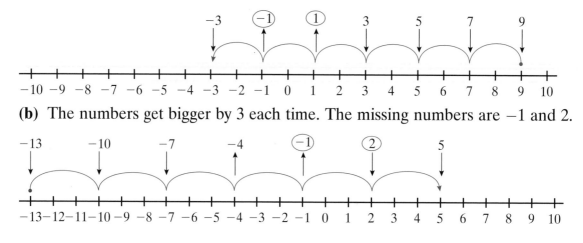

(b) The numbers get bigger by 3 each time. The missing numbers are -1 and 2.

Exercise 10H

1   Write down these numbers in order of size, starting with the smallest:

    (a) $2, -10, -2, -1, 5, -6.$ **(b)** $6, -3, 3, -4, 2, -9.$
    (c) $-5, 7, -8, 2, -2, -1.$ **(d)** $-2, 4, 9, -9, 1, -4.$
    (e) $4, -10, 1, 7, -11, -2.$ **(f)** $8, 1, -9, -3, -7, -6.$
    (g) $-8, 3, -6, 5, -9, -1.$ **(h)** $-19, 5, 18, -11, -3, -4.$

2 Work out the two missing numbers in each number pattern:

(a) 14, 11, 8, 5, ..., ..., −4   (b) −8, −6, −4, −2, ..., ..., 4

(c) 20, 16, 12, 8, ..., ..., −4   (d) −12, −8, −4, 0, ..., ..., 12

(e) 5, 2, −1, −4, ..., ..., −13   (f) −16, −13, −10, −7, ..., ..., 2

3 Write down all the numbers that are bigger than −6 and smaller than 3.

10.9 Continuing number patterns

Sometimes you need to continue a pattern of numbers.

■ **You can use a horizontal number line to continue number patterns.**

Example 20

Write down the next two numbers in this pattern:

   7, 4, 1, −2, ..., ...,

To get from one number to the next number in the pattern you subtract 3. The next two numbers in the pattern are −5 and −8.

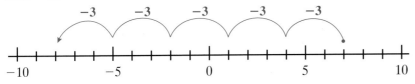

Example 21

Write down the two missing numbers in each sequence:
(a) −7, −5, −3, −1, ..., ..., 5.
(b) 14, 11, 8, 5, ..., ..., −4.

(a) You have to add 2 each time.
The missing numbers are 1 and 3.

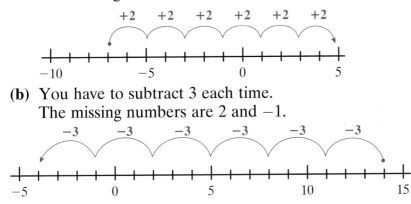

(b) You have to subtract 3 each time.
The missing numbers are 2 and −1.

Exercise 10I

Use a horizontal number line to help you with these questions.

1 Write down the next two numbers in each pattern:
- **(a)** 5, 3, 1, −1, . . .
- **(b)** 7, 4, 1, −2, . . .
- **(c)** 16, 12, 8, 4, . . .
- **(d)** 9, 5, 1, −3, . . .
- **(e)** 3, 0, −3, −6, . . .
- **(f)** 6, 4, 2, 0 . . .
- **(g)** 7, 3, −1, −5, . . .
- **(h)** −3, −5, −7, −9, . . .

2 Write down the next two numbers in each pattern:
- **(a)** −6, −4, −2, 0, . . .
- **(b)** −10, −7, −4, −1, . . .
- **(c)** −9, −5, −1, 3, . . .
- **(d)** −7, −5, −3, −1, . . .
- **(e)** −11, −8, −5, −2, . . .
- **(f)** −14, −9, −4, 1, . . .
- **(g)** −12, −9, −6, −3, . . .
- **(h)** −11, −7, −3, 1, . . .

3 Write down the two missing numbers in each pattern:
- **(a)** 11, 9, 7, 5, . . . , . . . , −1.
- **(b)** 14, 10, 6, 2, . . . , . . . , −10.
- **(c)** 8, 5, 2, −1, . . . , . . . , −10.
- **(d)** −6, −4, −2, 0, . . . , . . . , 6.
- **(e)** −7, −4, −1, 2, . . . , . . . , 11.
- **(f)** −8, −3, 2, 7, . . . , . . . , 22.

Exercise 10J

Activities

1 You will need a calculator.
- **(a)** Step 1: Enter the number 24 on the calculator.
  Step 2: Use the calculator to subtract 3 and record the result from the calculator display.
  Step 3: Continue to subtract 3 and record the results.
  Step 4: Write down what you notice about the results.
- **(b)** Repeat part (a), but subtract 4 each time instead of 3.
- **(c)** Compare the results you obtain in parts (a) and (b).

2 Repeat question **1**, but in Step 1 enter the number 14 on the calculator.

Calculator
24

Hint:
To keep subtracting 3 enter:
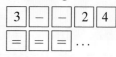

3 You need a calculator.

(a) Step 1: Enter the number −40 on the calculator.
Step 2: Use the calculator to add 4 and record
the result from the calculator display.
Step 3: Continue to add 4 and record the results.
Step 4: Write down what you notice about the
results.

(b) Repeat part (a), but add 5 each time instead of 4.

(c) Compare the results you obtain in parts (a) and (b).

4 Repeat question **3**, but in Step 1 enter the number −22
on the calculator.

Hint:
To enter "−40" on
your calculator:
Key in 40 then
press
the $\boxed{\pm}$ key.

Summary of key points

1 Positive numbers are greater than zero. They are sometimes written
with a plus sign. For example +2 or 2

2 Negative numbers are less than zero. They are written with a minus
sign. For example −5

3 You can use a vertical number line marked with
positive and negative numbers to

- find the highest and lowest values in a set of values
- write a list of values in order of size
- answer questions involving changes in values
- count on or back.

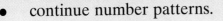

4 You can use a horizontal number line to answer questions about
positive and negative numbers. The smallest number is always on the
left.

5 You can use a horizontal number
line to
- write positive and negative
numbers in order
- continue number patterns.

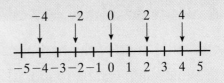

11 Graphs

11.1 Coordinates in the first quadrant

This grid shows the position of ships in a harbour.
You can describe where each one is using coordinates.

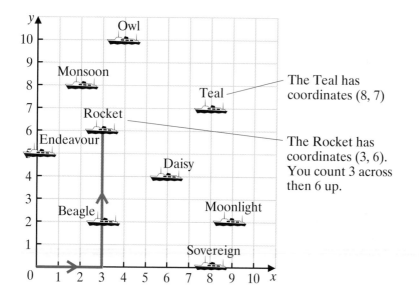

The Teal has coordinates (8, 7)

The Rocket has coordinates (3, 6). You count 3 across then 6 up.

■ **You can give the position of a place on a grid using coordinates.**

Remember:
Always count across first and then up.
Across (like the red) first, then up (like the blue).

Exercise 11A

Look at the map of the harbour.

1   Which ship can be found at:
    (a) (8, 0)
    (b) (6, 4)
    (c) (2, 8)
    (d) (9, 2)

2 What are the coordinates of these ships?

(a) Owl

(b) Endeavour

(c) Beagle

3 Write down the coordinates of the corners of the shape shown.

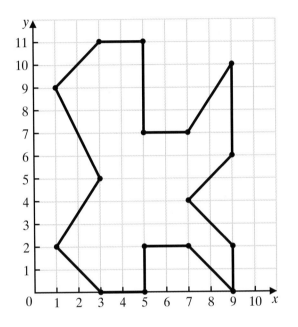

4 Write down the coordinates of the corners of each shape.

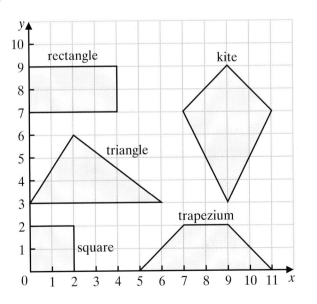

11.2 Plotting coordinates

You can draw your own grid on squared paper and plot coordinates on it.

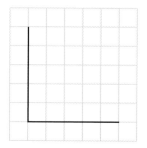

Draw two lines on squared paper as above. These lines are called **axes**.

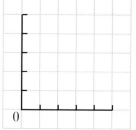

Mark each axis like this. Where the axes cross, write 0.

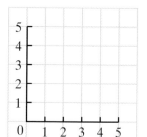

Number each axis from 0 to 5. Write the numbers in order.

Hint:
Axes is the plural of **axis**.

The point (0,0) is called the **origin**.

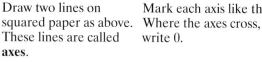

■ **The horizontal axis is the x-axis**
   The vertical axis is the y-axis

Hint: x is a**cross**

Example 1

Draw a coordinate grid.
Number each axis from 0 to 10.
Plot these points on your grid:

(2, 1);   (8, 1);   (8, 7);   (2, 7)

Join each point in order.
Join the last point to the first.
What shape do you get?

The shape is a square.

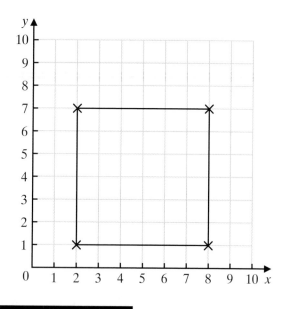

Exercise 11B

1   Draw a coordinate grid and number it from 0 to 10 on both axes. Plot the points:

   (6, 1), (9, 3), (9, 6), (6, 8), (3, 6), (3, 3), (6, 1)

   Join them up in order.
   What shape have you drawn?

2 Draw a coordinate grid and number both axes from 0 to 10. For each set of points:
- Plot the points on your grid
- Join the points up in order
- Shade in the shape

(a) (1, 7), (2, 7), (2, 8), (4, 8), (4, 7), (5, 7), (5, 9), (1, 9), (1, 7)

(b) (1, 0), (2, 0), (3, 1), (3, 2), (2, 3), (1, 3), (0, 2), (0, 1), (1, 0)

(c) (4, 1), (7, 4), (10, 4), (10, 1), (4, 1)

(d) (8, 5), (9, 5), (9, 7), (10, 7), (10, 8), (9, 8), (9, 10), (8, 10), (8, 8), (7, 8), (7, 7), (8, 7), (8, 5)

(e) (1, 4), (1, 6), (2, 6), (2, 5), (6, 5), (6, 6), (7, 6), (7, 4), (1, 4)

3 Draw a coordinate grid and number each axis from 0 to 10. Plot the points and join them up in order.

(1, 0), (1, 8), (2, 10), (3, 8), (3, 6), (8, 6), (8, 8), (9, 10), (10, 8), (10, 0), (7, 0), (7, 3), (6, 4), (5, 4), (4, 3), (4, 0), (1, 0).

4 Draw your own coordinate picture on a 0 to 10 grid. Write down the coordinates of each corner.

11.3 Lines on graphs

The grid opposite shows the starting points of counters in a game.

The red counters (G, H, I and J) are in a straight line.

Their coordinates are:

$$J \longrightarrow (7, 1)$$
$$I \longrightarrow (7, 3)$$
$$H \longrightarrow (7, 5)$$
$$G \longrightarrow (7, 7)$$

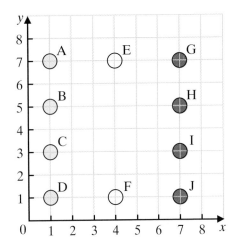

Each counter has an x-coordinate of 7. Any counter on this line will have the same x-coordinate.

You say that the **equation of the line** is $x = 7$.

Example 2

What is the equation of the line joining the counters D, F and J?

Look at the coordinates:

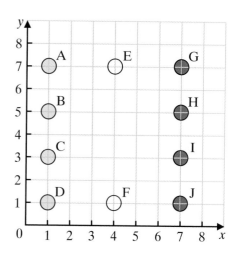

$$D \longrightarrow (1, 1)$$
$$F \longrightarrow (4, 1)$$
$$J \longrightarrow (7, 1)$$

They all have y-coordinate $= 1$.
The equation of the line is $y = 1$.

Exercise 11C

Part way through a game the counters are in the positions shown.

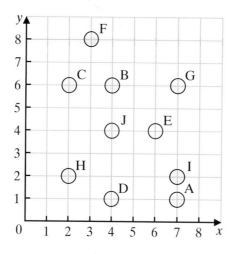

1 List the coordinates for each counter.

2 Name the lines joining:

    (a) Counters C, B and G   **(b)** Counters C and H

    (c) Counters B, J and D   **(d)** Counters H and I

    (e) Counters G, I and A   **(f)** Counters D and A

'Name the lines …' just means to give the equation of the lines.

3 Look at the grid. Name the lines joining the points:

(a) ABCD ($y =$)
(b) DEJ ($x =$)
(c) AM
(d) GFE
(e) COP
(f) LMNO
(g) HIJ
(h) FK
(i) GHL
(j) QP

4 Write down the equation of each of the coloured lines on this grid:

5 A gardener is planning a new flower bed. She uses a coordinate grid to help her plan.

Name the lines formed by each colour flower.

(a) purple (1 line)
(b) blue (2 lines)
(c) yellow (2 lines)
(d) red (4 lines)

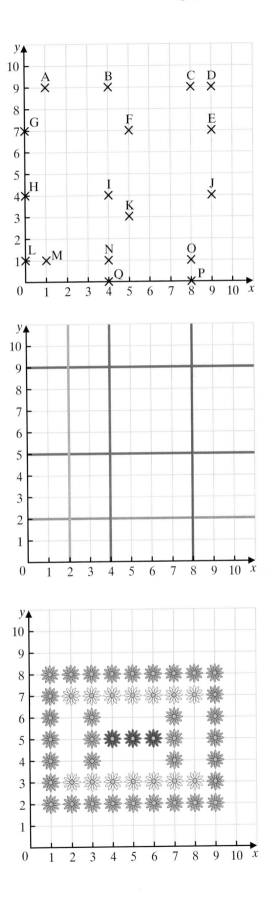

6 Name the lines formed by each set of points:

(a) (3, 1), (3, 4), (3, 7)   (b) (2, 4), (3, 4), (6, 4)
(c) (0, 2), (1, 2), (4, 2)   (d) (6, 3), (6, 4), (6, 6)
(e) (0, 1), (2, 1), (7, 1)   (f) (0, 0), (6, 0), (8, 0)
(g) (7, 2), (7, 7), (7, 9)   (h) (0, 1), (0, 5), (0, 8)

7 Draw a coordinate grid and number both axes from 0 to 10. Draw and label the following lines:

(a) $x = 4$ (b) $x = 7$
(c) $y = 3$ (d) $x = 2$
(e) $y = 6$ (f) $y = 7$
(g) $x = 5$ (h) $y = 1$

11.4 Coordinates in all 4 quadrants

The map shows an island with the ambulance station in the middle. You can describe where other places are by saying whether they are to the right or left and up or down from the ambulance station.

You do this by using coordinates with positive and negative numbers.

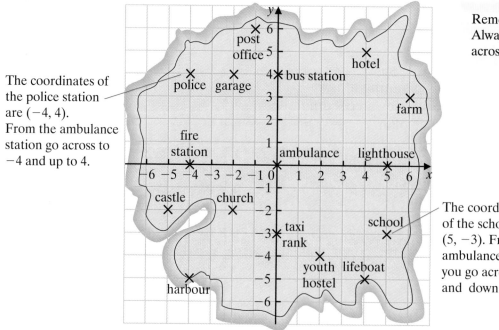

The coordinates of the police station are $(-4, 4)$. From the ambulance station go across to -4 and up to 4.

Remember: Always go across first.

The coordinates of the school are $(5, -3)$. From the ambulance station you go across to 5 and down to -3.

Exercise 11D

1 Look at the map of the island. What is at:
(a) $(5, 0)$ **(b)** $(4, 5)$ **(c)** $(2, -4)$ **(d)** $(4, -5)$
(e) $(-5, -2)$ **(f)** $(-2, 4)$ **(g)** $(-4, -5)$ **(h)** $(0, 0)$

2 What are the coordinates of:
(a) fire station **(b)** taxi rank **(c)** bus station
(d) post office **(e)** church **(f)** farm

3 Write down the coordinates of all the corner points of this shape:

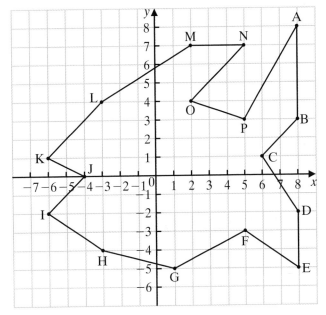

4 Part way through a netball match the players are in the positions shown.
Write down the coordinates of the players on both teams.

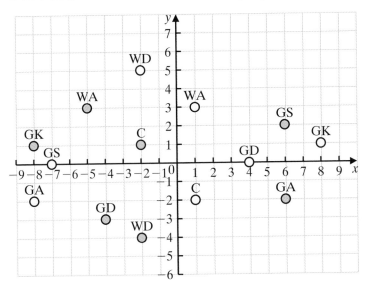

11.5 Drawing coordinate grids

You sometimes need to draw your own coordinate grid.
Draw two perpendicular axes to make a cross:

Label the axes:

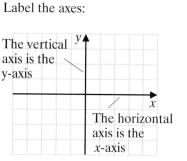

The vertical axis is the y-axis

The horizontal axis is the x-axis

Mark where the axes meet:

You label this with a zero

Remember this point is called the origin.

Number the axes:

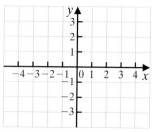

Write the positive numbers first, then the negative numbers.

Exercise 11E

1   Draw a coordinate grid from −8 to 8 on each axis.
    Plot each set of points and join them up as you go.

    (a) (6, 4), (8, 4), (8, 8), (6, 8), (6, 4)
    (b) (3, −4), (6, −4), (8, −1), (5, −1), (3, −4)
    (c) (−8, 8), (−8, 4), (−5, 8), (−8, 8)
    (d) (−7, 2), (0, 2), (0, −5), (−7, −5), (−7, 2)

    Name as many of the shapes as you can.

2   Draw a coordinate grid from −8 to 8 on each axis.
    Plot and label the following.

    lighthouse (7, −4),   factory (−2, 6),   shop (0, 0)
    school (−3, 5),   bus station (4, −3),   hospital (3, −2),
    train station (4, 5),   fairground (−3, −4),
    hotel (−4, 6),   church (5, 0),   garage (−4, 0)

3   Draw your own island on a grid and mark on some
    places of interest.
    Describe where things are on your island by using
    coordinates.

11.6 Using conversion graphs

■   **A graph shows a relationship on a coordinate grid**

Here is a conversion graph that you can use to convert
degrees Fahrenheit (°F) to degrees Celsius (°C).

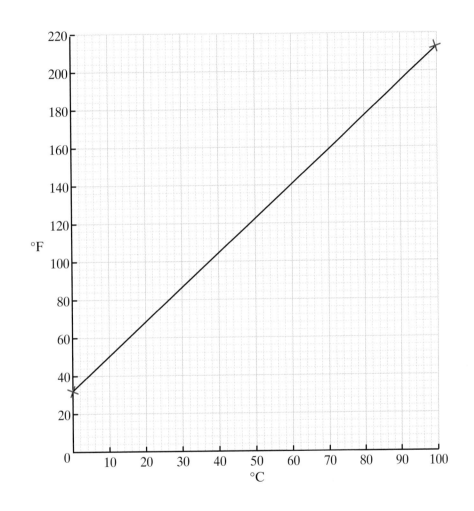

■   **You can use a conversion graph to convert from one
measurement to another**

Example 3

Using the conversion graph on page 177, convert:
(a) 80°C into Fahrenheit
(b) 126°F into Celsius

(a)

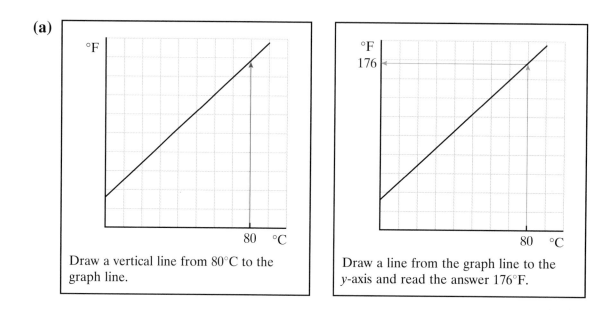

Draw a vertical line from 80°C to the graph line.

Draw a line from the graph line to the *y*-axis and read the answer 176°F.

(b)

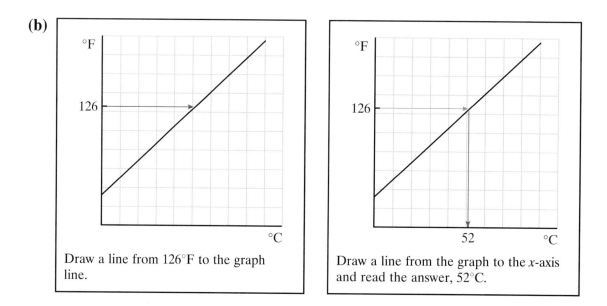

Draw a line from 126°F to the graph line.

Draw a line from the graph to the *x*-axis and read the answer, 52°C.

Exercise 11F

1   Copy the conversion graph on page 177 on to 2 mm
squared paper. Use the graph to convert:

(a) 30°C into °F   (b) 50°C into °F
(c) 90°C into °F   (d) 80°F into °C
(e) 160°F into °C   (f) 100°F into °C

2   This conversion graph converts between kilometres and
miles.
Copy it on to 2 mm squared paper and use it to convert:

(a) 100 km to miles   (b) 40 miles to km
(c) 70 miles to km   (d) 40 km to miles
(e) 64 km to miles   (f) 22 miles to km

Hint:
1 small square
represents
→ 2 miles
↑ 2 km

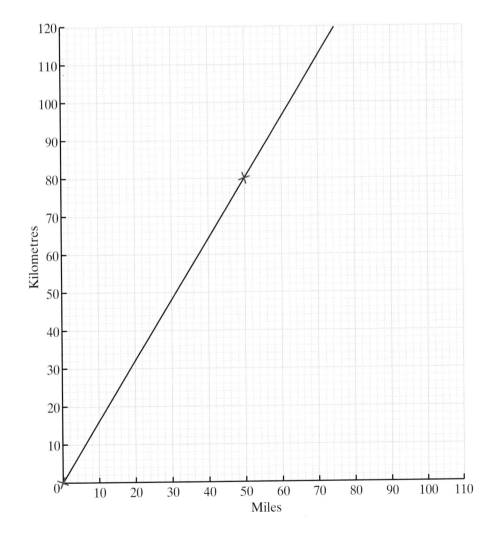

3 This conversion graph converts between millimetres
and inches.
Use the graph to convert:

(a) 2 inches into mm
(b) 10 inches into mm
(c) 200 mm into inches
(d) 10 mm into inches
(e) 1 inch into mm

Scale:
x-axis: 1 small square = 0.2 inches
y-axis: 1 small square = 10 mm

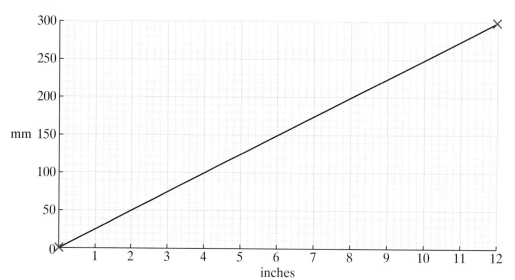

4 This conversion graph shows the relationship between
pints and litres. Use the graph to work out:

(a) how many litres is 10 pints
(b) how many litres is 50 pints
(c) how many pints is 1 litre
(d) how many pints is 20 litres

Scale:
x-axis: 1 small square = 2 pints
y-axis: 1 small square = 1 litre

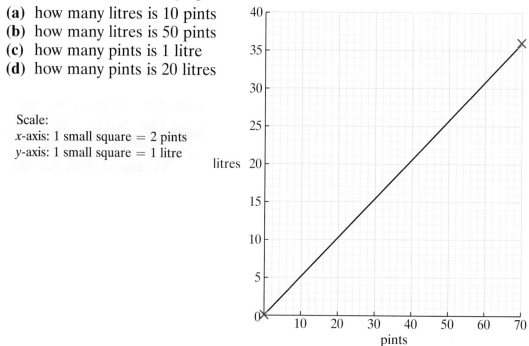

5 This conversion graph converts between kilograms (kg)
and pounds (lb).
Use the graph to convert:

(a) 20 kg into lbs   **(b)** 40 kg into lbs

(c) 30 lbs into kg   **(d)** 75 lbs into kg

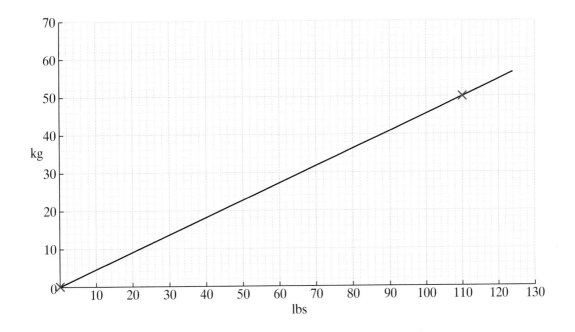

Summary of key points

1 You can give the position of a place on a grid using coordinates.

2 The horizontal axis is the x-axis.
The vertical axis is the y-axis.

3 A graph shows a relationship on a coordinate grid.

4 You can use a conversion graph to convert from one measurement to another.

12 Handling data

Information can be presented in different ways such as lists, tables and graphs.

A dictionary is a list of words:

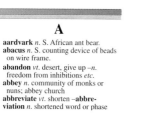

This graph shows some students' favourite sports:

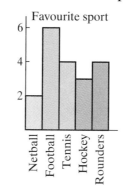

This table shows the results of tossing a coin:

Result:	Tally:
Heads	IIII IIII
Tails	IIII IIII I

■ **Data is another word for information.**

12.1 Collecting and organizing data

Tony asked thirty students' what their favourite subject was:

DT	Maths	Science	English	Maths
English	Science	English	Maths	Science
DT	English	Maths	Science	English
Maths	Science	English	Maths	Science
Science	English	Science	English	DT
English	Maths	English	Science	English

He used a frequency table to organize his data:

A frequency table is another name for a tally chart.

Subject	Tally	Frequency
English	IIII IIII I	11
Maths	IIII II	7
Science	IIII IIII	9
DT	III	3

Count up the tally marks. Put the total in the frequency column.

Bunch the tally marks in 5's. Then they are easier to count.

■ **You can collect data using a survey.**
■ **You can use a tally chart to organize data**
■ **A frequency table is another name for a tally chart**

Exercise 12A

1   This tally chart shows the number of letters delivered
   to 'Cliff Top' one week:

Method	Tally	Frequency
Monday	ⵑⵑ ⵑⵑ ||	12
Tuesday		7
Wednesday		9
Thursday		8
Friday		11
Saturday		8

   (a) Copy the tally chart and complete the tally column,
       (the first one is done for you).
   (b) How many letters were delivered altogether that
       week?
   (c) On which days were an even number of letters
       delivered?
   (d) On which day were the least number of letters
       delivered?

2   This frequency table shows how pupils in 8B get to
   school:

Method	Tally	Frequency
Walk	ⵑⵑ ||||	9
Bus	ⵑⵑ ||	
Car		6
Bicycle	|||	
Taxi	|	1
Train		
Total		30

Copy and complete the table.

3 Here are the results of Tom's survey on favourite drinks.

coke, tea, coke, milk, tea, orange, chocolate, coke, tea,
coffee, tea, orange, milk, chocolate, tea, coke, water,
milk, lemonade, orange, coffee, water, milk, coke,
lemonade, tea, coke, orange, milk, coffee, tea, coke,
lemonade, chocolate, milk, tea, orange, coke, coke, tea,
coffee, milk, chocolate, coke, water, coffee, lemonade,
tea, coke, milk.

Draw a frequency table to organize this data.

4 Rachel asked some pupils to choose a number between
0 and 10. Here are the results:

5	8	2	9	6	3	7	3	2	9
8	1	7	1	4	1	5	1	7	8
4	5	3	3	6	1	8	4	7	3
9	5	1	6	2	3	7	4	9	5
9	3	7	5	4	8	2	4	1	3
6	3	6	8	5	8	3	2	1	8
9	1	3	8	6	1	5	3	4	8
6	7	3	2	5	1	4	6	6	2

Draw up a frequency table to organize this data.

5 Julian asked his friends to name their favourite flower.
This list shows what they chose.

rose, daffodil, tulip, rose, orchid, crocus,
bluebell, rose, daffodil, lily, dahlia, orchid,
daffodil, rose, iris, tulip, orchid, iris, tulip,
dahlia, lily, tulip, lily, daffodil, crocus, iris,
dahlia, tulip, rose, lily, daffodil, tulip,
crocus, daffodil, lily, rose, rose, daffodil,
crocus, iris, orchid, tulip, rose, tulip,
crocus, rose, lily, daffodil, rose, tulip.

(a) Draw a frequency table with this information.
(b) How many replies did Julian get?
(c) Which flower was the most popular?
(d) How many people chose tulips?

6 Do a survey and draw a frequency table to show the
shoe sizes of pupils in your class.

12.2 Displaying data

Here are examples of some ways you can display data.

Hamid counted the number of different vehicles which passed as he waited for his bus.
This frequency table shows the result:

Vehicle	Tally	Frequency
Car	IIII III	8
Lorry	IIII	4
Bus	II	2
Motorcycle	IIII	5
Van	III	3
Bicycle	I	1

Hamid used these results to draw a pictogram.

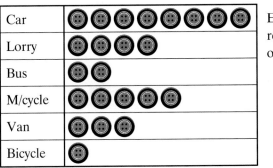

Each represents one vehicle

Always remember to include a key for your pictogram.

■ **A pictogram uses pictures to show data.**

Hamid also drew a bar chart:

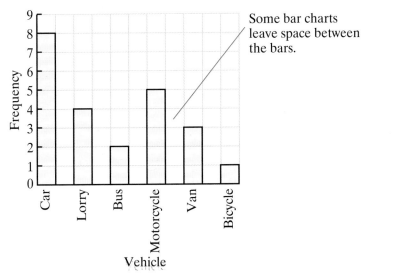

Some bar charts leave space between the bars.

Remember: All the bars should be the same width.

■ **A bar chart uses bars or blocks to show data.**

Hamid could also have drawn a bar-line graph:

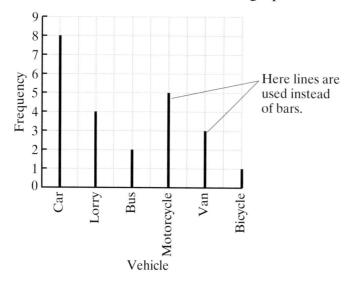

Here lines are used instead of bars.

■ **A bar line graph uses lines to show data.**

Exercise 12B

1   This pictogram shows the amount of pocket money spent by Rita one week.

Item	Money spent
CDs	£ £ £ £ £ £ £
Travel	£ £ £
Magazines	£ £
Cinema	£ £
Sweets	£
Swimming	£ £

£ represents £1

The key tells you how to read the pictogram.

(a) How much did Rita spend on:
      (i) CDs   (ii) magazines?
(b) How much money did she spend altogether?
(c) Draw a bar chart to show this data.

2 This horizontal bar chart shows the number of drinks ordered at Peter's café one lunchtime:

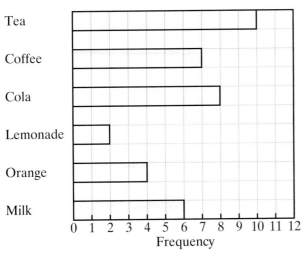

(a) How many drinks were ordered altogether?
(b) How many more people ordered tea than lemonade?
(c) If cola cost 24 p per glass, how much was spent on cola?

3 This bar-line graph shows the temperature in different cities on the same day:

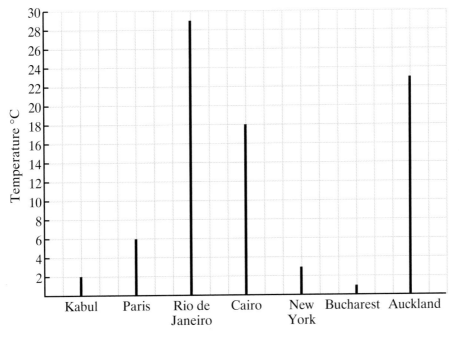

(a) Which city was hottest?
(b) Which cities were colder than 20°C?

4 Anthea asked her class which television channel they had watched between 6 pm and 7 pm the previous evening. The replies were:

> BBC1, ITV, ITV, ITV, CH4, BBC1, CH4,
> ITV, BBC1, BBC2, CH5, ITV, CH4, BBC2,
> ITV, BBC1, None, BBC1, CH5, ITV, None,
> CH4, BBC1, BBC1, ITV, CH4, BBC2.

(a) Complete a frequency table.
(b) Draw a pictogram to represent the data.
(c) Draw a bar graph.
(d) Which did you find easier to draw? Give a reason.

> A bar graph is the same as a bar chart

5 Raj counted the number of different types of tree he could see from his bedroom window. The results were:

Type	Oak	Chestnut	Elm	Cherry	Ash	Sycamore
Number	8	6	2	5	3	7

Show this data on:
(a) A pictogram.
(b) A bar-line graph.

6 Pupils of 8B listed their main hobby. The results are shown in the table.

Hobby	Computer games	Cooking	Music	Reading	Sport	Making models
Number	3	4	8	4	9	2

(a) Draw a pictogram to show this data.
(b) Draw a bar chart showing this information.

12.3 Dealing with larger numbers

The number of patients visiting a doctor's surgery were:

Day	Mon	Tues	Wed	Thur	Fri	Sat
Number	32	28	36	30	26	24

You can show this information in a bar chart:

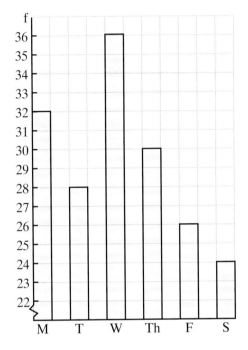

You mark the vertical scale like this:

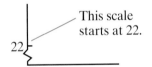

This scale starts at 22.

This shows that it doesn't start at zero.

Exercise 12C

1   This bar graph shows the number of phone calls Kim
    received one week.

   (a) How many phone calls did she
       receive altogether?
   (b) On which days did she have the
       same number of calls?
   (c) How many calls did she have
       on Sunday?

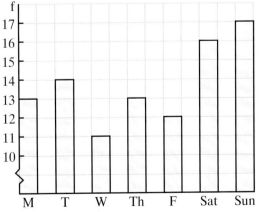

2 This table shows how many books Heidi borrowed from the local library:

Month	Jan	Feb	Mar	Apr	May	Jun	Jul
Visits	16	24	20	26	28	22	18

Hint:
If ⊞ represents 4 books then ⊟ represents 2 books.

Show this information by:

(a) drawing a pictogram (use ⊞ to represent 4 books)

(b) drawing a bar chart.

3 This table shows the number of pupils who were away from school during one week.

Day	Mon	Tues	Wed	Thur	Fri
Number	28	33	22	38	26

Draw a bar graph to represent this data.

4 The number of books sold in the first hour in a bookshop last week was:

Day	Mon	Tues	Wed	Thur	Fri	Sat
Number	40	32	36	28	30	34

(a) Using ⊞ to represent 8 books, draw a pictogram.

(b) Draw a bar chart to show this data.

5 The number of people entering a swimming pool one morning is shown in the table.

1st hour	2nd hour	3rd hour	4th hour	5th hour	6th hour
24	36	45	39	27	30

Hint:
Think how you could represent 3 people.

(a) Draw a horizontal bar chart to represent this data.

(b) Using ⬡ to represent 6 people, draw a pictogram to show this data.

6 The number of trains leaving London railway stations
in the rush hour are:

Waterloo	72	Charing Cross	68	Paddington	45
Cannon Street	54	Euston	58	Kings Cross	42
Marylebone	40	Liverpool Street	56		

(a) Draw *two* different diagrams to represent this data.
(b) Which diagram do you think is the best?
Give your reason.

7 This list shows the temperatures, in Fahrenheit,
one day in April:

London	57	Aberdeen	46
Alicante	64	Barbados	86
Gibraltar	70	Venice	57
Athens	67	Tokyo	76

Draw a bar-line graph to show this information.

12.4 Dual bar graphs

When you compare more than one set of data it is useful to
draw a dual bar chart.

Example 1

Nicola and Jenny drew a dual bar graph to compare their
exam results.

	English	Maths	Science	German	History	French
Nicola	55	60	55	48	50	74
Jenny	68	72	50	45	62	44

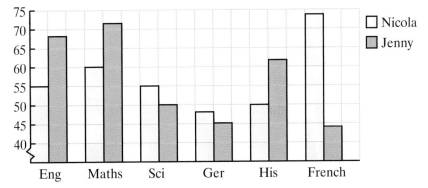

■ **Dual bar graphs are used to compare two sets of data
on the same topic**

Exercise 12D

1 This graph shows the number of bikes sold by
Cycles Ltd over six weeks:

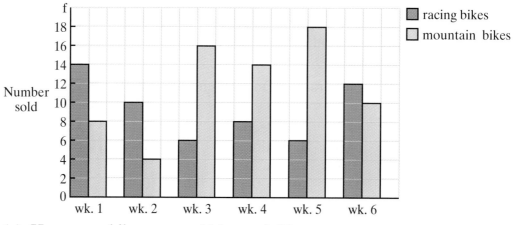

(a) How many bikes were sold in week 3?
(b) How many mountain bikes were sold in week 1?
(c) Which week were the most bikes sold?
(d) Which week was a total of fourteen bikes sold?
(e) Which weeks were more racing bikes sold than
mountain bikes?
(f) How many bikes were sold altogether?

2 Paula and Gita counted the number of different birds
they saw on their way to school. The result was:

	Wren	Pigeon	Sparrow	Robin	Starling	Blackbird
Paula	4	7	5	0	6	2
Gita	2	4	6	1	7	1

(a) Draw a dual bar graph to compare their data.
(b) How many birds did they see altogether?
(c) How many did Gita see?
(d) Which were the most common birds seen?
(e) Who saw the most Sparrows?

3 The number of rooms available during one week in two
hotels was:

	Mon	Tues	Wed	Thur	Fri	Sat	Sun
Clifftop	6	2	3	5	1	0	7
Seaview	3	4	2	2	3	2	5

(a) Draw a dual bar graph to show this data.
(b) How many rooms were available altogether?
(c) On which night were there fewest rooms to let?
(d) Which is the easiest night to book a room:
    (i) at Clifftop?   **(ii)** at Seaview?

12.5 Types of data

Data that changes over time can be shown on a line graph.

When you draw a line graph you need to decide whether the data is **discrete** or **continuous**.

■ **Data you count is called discrete data**
    e.g. Susan planted three trees in the garden.
        Karl has one kitten called Smokey.

■ **Data you can measure is called continuous data**
    e.g. The tallest tree is 2.5 metres high.
        Smokey weighs 1.2 kilograms.

■ **Line graphs can be used to show continuous data**

Example 2

The graph shows the number of people leaving a sports ground by various gates.

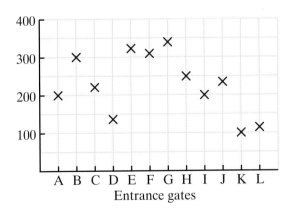

The data is discrete so you do not join up the points. A person cannot leave between gates!

Example 3

The line graph shows the temperature in Aaran's fishtank over 8 days:

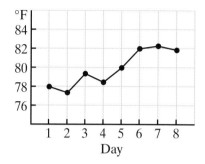

The data is continuous so the plotted points are joined up.

Exercise 12E

1   State whether the following are discrete or continuous.
    (a) The number of pupils in 8A.
    (b) The weight of cherries in the bag.
    (c) The time it took Steve to run the race.
    (d) The number of pupils in the school orchestra.
    (e) The amount of rain that fell last night.
    (f) The number of people on the bus.
    (g) The height of a lampost.
    (h) The cost of a telephone call.
    (i) The temperature.
    (j) The speed of a train.

2   The graph shows the average temperature in Sudbury over a twelve-month period.

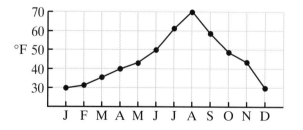

    (a) Which was the hottest month?
    (b) What was the highest temperature recorded?
    (c) In which months did the temperature fall below 40°F?

3 Draw a line graph or bar chart to represent each of the following:

(a) The mid-day temperature, in °C, in Lampeter.

June	5th	6th	7th	8th	9th	10th
Temperature	22	25	27	24	25	28

(b) The number of pupils absent from school.

June	5th	6th	7th	8th	9th	10th
Number	17	24	20	25	18	21

(c) The number of ice creams sold during break.

September	3rd	4th	5th	6th	7th
Number	24	31	27	23	34

(d) The fall in value of a bicycle bought in 1980.

Year	1980	1981	1982	1983	1984	1985	1986	1987
Value	£185	£130	£100	£80	£65	£53	£43	£35

Can you estimate the value in 1988?

> **Hint:**
> You should draw a line graph for continuous data and a bar chart for discrete data.

4 The output of a motor cycle factory for the first five months of the year was:

Month	Jan	Feb	Mar	Apr	May
Output	110	122	138	145	162

(a) Draw a line graph to represent this data.

(b) Use the graph to estimate the number they will produce in June.

(c) Give a reason why your estimate may be:
   (i) too high   **(ii)** too low.

12.6 Grouping data

It is sometimes easier to spot patterns in data if you record it in groups. These groups are often called class intervals and must not overlap.

Example 4

You could group examination marks like this:

1–10, 11–20, 21–30 and so on up to 91–100.

It is usual to make the class intervals the same size.

Example 5

Class 8B take a spelling test.

The data for their results is split into eight groups:

Marks	Tally	Frequency
0–1	||	2
2–3	||||	4
4–5	⊬|	5
6–7	⊬| |	6
8–9	⊬|	5
10–11	||||	4
12–13	|||	3
14–15	|||	3

It is sensible to use between four and ten groups.
Here the data has been split into eight groups.

The bar graph shows the results:

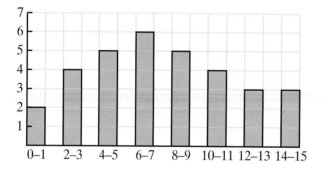

If the data was grouped into four ...

Marks	Tally	Frequency
0–3	⊬| |	6
4–7	⊬| ⊬| |	11
8–11	⊬| ||||	9
12–15	⊬| |	6

... the bar graph would look like this:

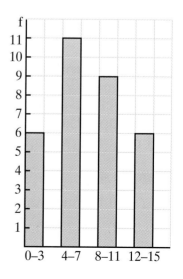

It is easier to draw conclusions from this last graph,
e.g. that the most common mark for the test was between
4 and 7, that 15 pupils score more than half marks and
17 less than half marks.

■ **Data which has a wide range of values is usually
grouped into class intervals.**

■ **Class intervals are usually the same size and must not
overlap.**

Exercise 12F

1   Thirty pupils took a general knowledge test. The results
were:

12	22	15	7	14
27	6	28	26	3
13	18	4	24	17
16	3	37	14	11
8	16	31	36	22
17	27	9	23	30

(a) Use the data to copy and complete the table.

Marks	Tally	Frequency
0–4		
5–9		
10–14		
15–19		
20–24		
25–29		
30–34		
35–39		

(b) Draw a bar chart to represent this data.
(c) Using class intervals 0–9, 10–19, 20–29, 30–39 draw
another bar graph.
(d) Which do you think is the most appropriate?
Give your reason.

2 The marks for 60 pupils in an English examination were:

```
 5  31  56  11  45  26  53  42  35  64
91  43   8  66  52  84  69  20  72  12
32  25  75  54  34  44  96  57  47  77
45  81  45  72  16  87   9  33  63  48
76  34  28  55  40  65  58  72  14  37
17  52  14   7  47  30  21  42  76  56
```

(a) Using class intervals 0–9, 10–19, 20–29, etc. draw up a frequency table.

(b) Draw a bar chart.

(c) Write down two conclusions from your bar chart.

3 The same pupils marks in the Maths examination were:

```
52  44  63  62   9  25  39  46  63  71
38  35  84  15  45  94  70  29  85  62
45  36  65  48  49  30   8  45  52   7
61  91  54  81  12  81  59  48  76  46
74  45  23  63  58  32  97  50  68  77
26  56  11  51  60  73  25  46  34  53
```

(a) Using class intervals 0–9, 10–19, 20–29, etc., draw up a frequency table.

(b) Draw a bar chart to represent this data.

(c) Write down two observations comparing the English and Maths charts.

4 The length, in seconds, of telephone calls to John's office one morning were:

```
 36  124   27   68   15   34
 59   63   38   22   84   26
105   24  184   29   26  157
216   51   11  134   53   45
 15  132   45   73  105   82
```

(a) Using class intervals of 1–29, 30–59, 60–99 etc. draw up a frequency table.

(b) Draw a bar graph.

(c) Comment on your result.

5 The number of goals scored by teams in a league were:

```
16  25  20   9  21  22   8  12
20  17   8  12  19  21  23  14
19  15  28  16   4  13  29   7
10  26  22  19  20  26  24  11
18  21  13  24  16  23  14  22
```

(a) Using class intervals 1–5, 6–10, 11–15, 16–20, 21–25, 26–30 construct a frequency table.

(b) Draw a bar graph.

(c) Comment on your graph.

6 In a three day fishing competition the number of fish caught by the anglers were:

```
 6  25   2  13  22  13  10  16
17  14  11   5  22   4  12  14
12   1  18  11  12  10  16   3
 7  15   6   7  14   1   9  12
 3  17   4  15   8  19  22   8
```

(a) Choose a suitable class interval and draw a bar graph.

(b) Write down two observations from your graph.

7 The number of people entering a shopping mall each minute in the first hour was:

```
36  25  28  12  40  23  19  30  29  17
44  35  18  30  26  42   9  11  27  23
28  33  19  37  48  36  33  28  31  29
35  16  19  25  23  41  37  25  38  21
47  35  15  36  19   8  23  27  33  35
27  18  25  36  22  40  38  26  13  24
```

(a) Choose a suitable class interval and draw a bar graph.

(b) Write down two observations from your graph.

Summary of key points

1   Data is another word for information.

2   You can collect data using a survey.

3   You can use a tally chart to organize data.

4   A frequency table is another name for a tally chart.

5   A pictogram uses pictures to show data.

6   A bar chart uses bars or blocks to show data.

7   A bar line graph uses lines to show data.

8   Dual bar graphs are used to compare two sets of data on the same topic.

9   Data you count is called discrete data
    e.g. Susan planted three trees in the garden.
    Karl has one kitten called Smokey.

10 Data you can measure is called continuous data
    e.g. The tallest tree is 2.5 metres high.
    Smokey weighs 1.2 kilograms.

11 Line graphs can be used to show continuous data.

12 Data which has a wide range of values is usually grouped into class intervals.

13 Class intervals are usually the same size and must not overlap.

13 Formulae and equations

Formulae are often used in everyday life. When you are in a car, your speed is worked out by this formula:

$$\text{speed} = \frac{\text{distance travelled}}{\text{time taken}}$$

50 mph means you travel 50 **m**iles **p**er **h**our.

13.1 Word formulae

You can use word formulae to help solve problems.

Example 1

Jerome buys some ice-creams. This formula describes the total cost:

total cost of ice-creams = cost of one ice-cream × number bought

Jerome buys 5 ice-creams at 90p each. Use the formula to find the total cost of the ice-creams.

cost of ice-creams = cost of one ice-cream × number bought
$$= \qquad 90p \qquad \times \qquad 5$$
$$= 450p$$
$$= £4.50$$

Sometimes you will need to write your own word formulae.

Example 2

Write a word formula to find the cost of bananas. Use it to find the cost of 6 bananas at 25p each.

total cost of bananas = cost of one banana × number bought
$$= \qquad 25p \qquad \times \qquad 6$$
$$= 150p$$
$$= £1.50$$

1 Andrew buys some rulers. He uses the formula:
> total cost of rulers = cost of one ruler × number bought.

The cost of one ruler is 35p. Andrew buys 2 rulers.
Work out the total cost of the rulers.

2 Diana buys some books. She uses the formula:
> total cost of books = cost of one × number bought.

Diana buys 3 books at £4 each.
Find the total cost of the books.

3 Leon buys some apples. He uses the formula:
> total cost of apples = cost of one apple × number bought.

Find the total cost of 7 apples at 20p each.

4 Mrs Ijaha uses this formula to find the cost of CDs:
> total cost of CDs = cost of one CD × number bought.

One CD costs £12. Work out the cost of 6 CDs.

5 Write a word formula to find the cost of oranges.
Use it to work out the cost of 4 oranges at 30p each.

6 Write a word formula to find the cost of choc bars.
Use it to calculate the cost of 5 choc bars at 35p each.

7 Write a word formula to find the cost of jars of coffee.
Use it to find the cost of 3 jars of coffee at £2.50 each.

8 Write a word formula to find the cost of video tapes.
Use it to work out the cost of 6 video tapes at £7 each.

13.2 Using letters to represent numbers

You can fit a red and purple
rod together ...

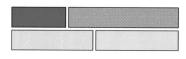

... to make the same length
as two green rods.

This mathematical sentence connects the lengths of the rods:

> length of red + length of purple = length of green + length of green

You can use letters for short:

> $r + p = g + g$
>
> or, $r + p = 2g$

2g means
$2 \times g$ *or* $g + g$

Exercise 13B

In this exercise either use a set of cuisenaire rods or trace the rods below.

Using these letters to stand for the lengths of the rods:

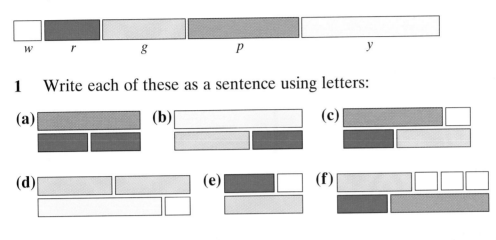

1   Write each of these as a sentence using letters:

(a)   (b)   (c)

(d)   (e)   (f)

2   Find all the different rod trains equal to the length of the purple rod. Write each one as a sentence using letters.

A **rod train** is any combination of rods in a row.
For example:

13.3 Using letters in formulae

■   **In formulae, unknown amounts can be replaced by letters for short.**

Example 3

One week Simon bought a stickers.
The next week he bought b more.
Altogether he bought s stickers.
Write a formula for the total number of stickers Simon bought.

total number of stickers = stickers bought one week + stickers bought next week

$$s = a + b$$

So the formula is $s = a + b$

Example 4

The height of the woman is w.
The height of the tree is t.
The height of the pyramid is p.

(a) Write a formula connecting the height of the tree and the woman.

(b) Write a formula connecting p and t.

This palm tree is 3 times taller than the woman.

This pyramid is twice as tall as the palm tree.

(a) $t = 3 \times w$
or $t = 3w$

(b) $p = 2 \times t$
or $p = 2t$

Exercise 13C

1   Wai is x years old. His sister Yen is y years old. Their total age is t. Write a formula for the total age of Wai and Yen.

2   James works in a newsagents.
He gets £5 for each hour he works.
Last week James worked n hours. His total pay is p.
Write a formula for his pay.

3   The perimeter of a flat shape is the total distance around the edge of the shape.
Write formulae for the perimeters P of these shapes:

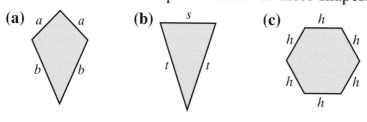

(a) a a b b **(b)** s t t **(c)** h h h h h h

Hint:
Each formula should begin $P =$

4   The temperature in Arizona is $a°C$.
The temperature in Nevada is $n°C$.
The difference between the temperatures in Arizona and Nevada is $d°C$.
Write a formula connecting a, n and d.

5 This recipe shows how to make marble cake.
Write a formula to find the total time *t* before
the cake is ready to serve.

> **Marble Cake:**
>
> Mix all ingredients.
> Beat mixture for *c* minutes.
> Cook in oven for *d* minutes.
> Leave to cool for *e* minutes.
> Now ready to serve.

6 Mickey divides a bag of sweets equally between his
3 friends. There are *s* sweets in the bag. Each friend gets
f sweets each. Write a formula that connects *s* and *f*.

7 A poster is enlarged so that each side is
3 times its original size.
Write a formula connecting
m and *l*.

$\leftarrow l \rightarrow$

$\longleftarrow m \longrightarrow$

13.4 Formulae with two operations

Sometimes two operations are used in one formula.
You need to know which order to work operations out in to
get the right answer.
You can remember the correct order from the made up
word BIDMAS:

Brackets   Do brackets first . . .

Indices

Division

Multiplication

Addition   . . . and then work

Subtraction   down the list.

Remember:
Indices are 'to the
power of' numbers,
like 4^2 or 3^5.

You do the operation nearest to the top first and work
down the list.

Example 5

Work out:

(a) $3 \times 4 + 2$

(b) $2 + 3 \times 4$

You always do the multiplication first so the answer is the same for both:

(a) $3 \times 4 + 2$

$12 + 2 = 14$

(b) $2 + 3 \times 4$

$2 + 12 = 14$

Example 6

Work out $(3 + 4) + 12 \div 3$

Work out the brackets first:

$7 + 12 \div 3$ —————— $3 + 4 = 7$

Division comes next:

$7 + 4$ —————— $12 \div 3 = 4$

Now add to get the answer:

$7 + 4 = 11$

Exercise 13D

1 Work out:

(a) $3 \times 2 + 4$

(b) $3 \times (2 + 4)$

(c) $2 \times (5 + 6)$

(d) $2 + 5 \times 3$

(e) $(2 + 5) \times 3$

(f) $3 \times 2 + 2 \times 4$

(g) $3 \times (2 + 2) \times 4$

(h) $(5 - 4) \times 2$

(i) $5 + 4 \times 2$

(j) $14 - 3 \times 2$

(k) $(14 - 3) \times 2$

(l) $(10 - 5) \times 5$

Example 7

Jermaine joins a gym. He has to pay a joining fee and then £20 each month.

(a) Write this as a word formula. The total cost is t pounds. Calculate how much Jermaine pays in total if:

(b) the joining fee is £50 and he goes to the gym for 10 months,

(c) the joining fee is £30 and he goes for 12 months.

(a) total cost = joining fee + monthly charge × number of months

(b) total cost = £50 + £20 × 10

= £50 + £200

= £250

(c) total cost = £30 + £20 × 12

= £30 + £240

= £270

Remember:
you always × before
you +

Exercise 13E

1 Janine is a decorator. She charges £25 for materials plus £10 for each hour she works.

   (a) Write a word formula showing how much Janine charges.

   (b) Calculate how much Janine charges for a job taking 5 hours.

2 Parvez is thinking about buying a computer.

   (a) Work out the total cost for each model.

   (b) Which one is cheapest?

laptop

desktop computer

deposit £500
plus £200 per month
for 5 months

deposit £200
plus £100 per
month for
8 months

3 The instructions for cooking roast chicken are: '45 minutes for each kilogram the chicken weighs, then add another 40 minutes.'

   (a) Copy and complete this word formula:

   time to cook roast chicken =

   (b) How many minutes will it take to cook a chicken that weighs 4 kilograms?

13.5 Substituting into algebraic formulae

You can find answers to problems by substituting numbers into algebraic formulae.

Example 8

Jane throws a ball into the air.
The formula $s = 40 - 10t$ gives the speed of the ball,
s after time t seconds.

Work out the speed of the ball after:
(a) 1 second   **(b)** 2 seconds

Substitute for $t = 1$:   Substitute for $t = 2$:
$$s = 40 - 10 \times 1$$ $$s = 40 - 10 \times 2$$
$$= 40 - 10$$ $$= 40 - 20$$
$$= 30$$ $$= 20$$

Exercise 13F

1   The perimeter of a rectangle is given by the formula.
$$P = 2l + 2w$$
Work out the perimeter P, of a rectangle with:
(a) $l = 4, w = 3$ **(b)** $l = 5, w = 1$ **(c)** $l = 10, w = 4$

2   The area of a square is given by the formula
$$A = l^2$$
Work out the area A, of a square with:

Dont forget $l^2 = l \times l$

(a) $l = 3$ **(b)** $l = 5$ **(c)** $l = 10$

3   The perimeter of a rectangle can also be written using
the formula $P = 2 \times (l + w)$
Use this formula to work out the perimeter P when:
(a) $l = 5, w = 3$ **(b)** $l = 10, w = 2$ **(c)** $l = 8, w = 4$

4   The distance, D metres, travelled when a ball is
thrown into the air is given by the formula
$$D = (s^2 - 100) \div 20$$
Work out the distance travelled when s is:
(a) 20   **(b)** 10   **(c)** 12

Remember to use
Brackets
Indices
Division
Multiplication
Addition
Subtraction

5   The cost, c pounds, of printing paper with a
letterhead is given by the formula:
$$C = 20 + 0.05n$$
Work out C when n is:
(a) 100   **(b)** 1000   **(c)** 500   **(d)** 10 000

13.6 Solving equations

■ **Equations and formulae are different:**

An equation:

$x - 4 = 6$

This is only true when $x = 10$.
The **solution** to this equation is
$x = 10$

A formula:

total cost = cost of one CD
$\qquad\qquad\quad \times$ number bought

$t = c \times n$

This works for many different
values of c and n.

To solve an equation, you have to find the value of the letter.

Sometimes you can solve an equation just by using number facts.

Example 9

Solve the equation:

$\qquad 4 + m = 10$

You know that $4 + 6 = 10$, so the solution to this equation
is $m = 6$.

Spotting the solution like this is called solving the equation
by inspection.

Example 10

Solve this equation by inspection:

$\qquad 3 \times s = 12$

You know that $3 \times 4 = 12$, so $s = 4$.

Exercise 13G

Solve these equations by inspection:

You can solve these
equations just by
using number facts.

1 $a + 4 = 7$	**2** $b + 2 = 7$
3 $c + 2 = 5$	**4** $d + 3 = 8$
5 $5 + r = 14$	**6** $8 + s = 15$
7 $17 + t = 25$	**8** $5 + u = 19$
9 $m - 6 = 9$	**10** $n - 26 = 2$

11 $p - 3 = 3$	**12** $q - 6 = 15$
13 $9 - m = 2$	**14** $32 - n = 12$
15 $14 - p = 6$	**16** $15 - q = 9$
17 $2 \times r = 10$	**18** $5 \times s = 10$
19 $4 \times t = 12$	**20** $4 \times u = 8$
21 $3 \times v = 3$	**22** $6 \times w = 18$
23 $3 \times x = 9$	**24** $y \times 2 = 5$
25 $e \div 6 = 2$	**26** $f \div 5 = 4$
27 $g \div 3 = 3$	**28** $h \div 4 = 12$
29 $i \div 4 = 8$	**30** $j \div 5 = 5$
31 $k \div 6 = 6$	**32** $l \div 2 = 9$

13.7 Solving equations using number machines

Sometimes equations are too complicated to solve by inspection. One way is to use number machines.

Example 11

Solve the equation:

$$a + 7 = 18$$

You can write the equation using a number machine.

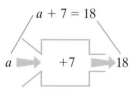

To solve the equation, use the inverse number machine:

> An **inverse** operation 'undoes' the original operation.
> -7 is the **inverse operation** of $+7$.
> There is more on inverses on page 81.

so $18 - 7 = a$
$$a = 11$$

Example 12

Solve these equations using inverse number machines:

(a) $w - 5 = 17$ **(b)** $8k = 24$ **(c)** $g \div 4 = 10$

(a)

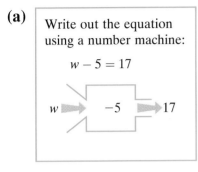

Write out the equation using a number machine:

$$w - 5 = 17$$

Write out the inverse: ($+5$ is the inverse of -5):

Solve the equation:

$$w - 5 = 17$$

so

$$17 + 5 = w$$

and

$$w = 22$$

So w is equal to 22.

(b) $8k = 24$

Write out the equation: Find the inverse:

Notice that

$$8k = k \times 8$$

Do the division to find the answer:

$$24 \div 8 = k$$

So $k = 3$

(c) $g \div 4 = 10$

Write out the equation: Find the inverse:

Do the division to find the answer:

$$10 \times 4 = g$$

So $g = 40$

Exercise 13H

Solve these equations using inverse number machines:

1 $m + 3 = 7$

2 $n + 6 = 11$

3 $p + 2 = 3$

4 $q + 6 = 13$

5 $r - 2 = 6$

6 $s - 5 = 4$

7 $t - 2 = 5$

8 $u - 7 = 8$

9 $2r = 40$

10 $5s = 35$

11 $10t = 100$

12 $12u = 84$

13 $i \div 4 = 0$

14 $j \div 4 = 4$

15 $k \div 4 = 6$

16 $l \div 4 = 20$

Hint:

operation	inverse
+	−
−	+
×	÷
÷	×

13.8 Using algebra to solve equations

You can also use algebra to solve equations.

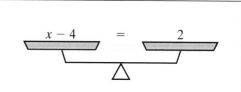

You can think of an equation as a balancing act – both sides of the equation are equal.

To solve $x - 4 = 2$ you must get x on its own on one side of the scales.

Add 4 to both sides:

adding 4 to **both** sides means the scales still balance

$-4 + 4 = 0$ leaving x on its own

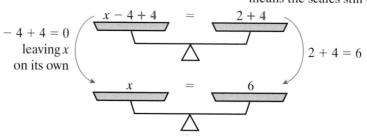

$2 + 4 = 6$

The scales balance when $x = 6$ so the solution of $x - 4 = 2$ is $x = 6$.

Exercise 13I

Solve these equations by using the balance method.

1	$a + 5 = 9$	**2**	$b + 6 = 12$	**3**	$c + 5 = 7$
4	$d + 8 = 20$	**5**	$e - 4 = 5$	**6**	$f - 3 = 7$
7	$g - 7 = 7$	**8**	$h - 3 = 5$	**9**	$5i = 15$
10	$6j = 18$	**11**	$3k = 12$	**12**	$4l = 12$
13	$m \div 4 = 2$	**14**	$n \div 2 = 5$	**15**	$p \div 3 = 5$

Using algebra to solve two-step equations

To solve $4x - 2 = 10$ you need to get x on its own on one side of the scales.

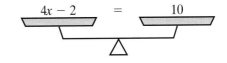

First add 2 to both sides:

adding 2 to **both** sides means the scales still balance

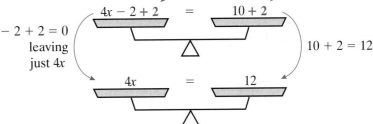

$-2 + 2 = 0$ leaving just $4x$

$10 + 2 = 12$

To get x on its own divide both sides by 4:

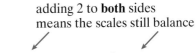

$4x \div 4 = x$

$12 \div 4 = 3$

The scales balance when $x = 3$.
$x = 3$ is the solution of $4x - 2 = 10$.

Example 13

Solve this equation using the balance method:

$$5x + 1 = 11$$
$$5x + 1 - 1 = 11 - 1 \quad \dots\dots\dots\dots \quad \text{First } -1 \text{ from both sides}$$
$$5x = 10$$
$$5x \div 5 = 10 \div 5 \quad \dots\dots\dots\dots \quad \text{Now divide both sides by 5}$$
$$x = 2$$

Exercise 13J

1 Work out:

   (a) $2a + 1 = 5$ **(b)** $3b - 2 = 7$ **(c)** $5c + 1 = 31$

   (d) $2d - 3 = 7$ **(e)** $3e + 3 = 12$ **(f)** $2f - 5 = 11$

   (g) $5g + 4 = 14$ **(h)** $4h - 3 = 17$ **(i)** $7i + 1 = 15$

   (j) $3j + 1 = 10$ **(k)** $5k + 7 = 32$ **(l)** $3l - 4 = 11$

   (m) $10m - 3 = 27$ **(n)** $4n - 6 = 30$ **(o)** $12o + 5 = 53$

2 Harry thought of a number.
He doubled the number and added 3
His answer was 13
What was Harry's original number?

3 Simone thought of a number.
She multiplied the number by 3 and added 1
Her answer was 13
What was Simone's original number?

4 Sunderfield United get 3 points for a win, 1 point for a draw and 0 points if they lose.
After they play 20 matches, they have 40 points.
They have won x matches and drawn 4 matches.
How many matches have they won?

5 The sum of 3 consecutive is numbers is 21
Find the numbers.

6 The sum of 2 consecutive odd numbers is 16
Find the two numbers.

Consecutive just means 'one after the other'.

Summary of key points

1 In formulae, unknown amounts can be replaced by letters for short.

2 Equations and formulae are different:

An equation:
$x - 4 = 6$
This is only true when $x = 10$
The solution to this equation is $x = 10$.

A formula:
total cost = cost of one CD $\times$ number bought
$t = c \times n$
This works for many different values of c and n.

3 You can solve equations by using inverse operations.

14 Perimeter, area and volume

14.1 Perimeter and area

Mr Khan has laid a patio.

He used square slabs with one metre sides.

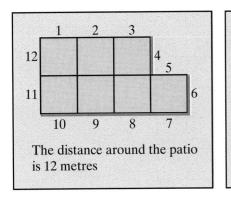

The distance around the patio is 12 metres

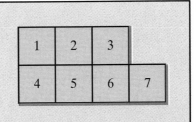

There are 7 slabs so the patio covers 7 square metres

Each slab is one square metre. You write 1 m².

- **The distance around a flat shape is the perimeter.**

- **The amount of space covered by a flat shape is the area.**

Example 1

Work out the perimeter and area of this shape:

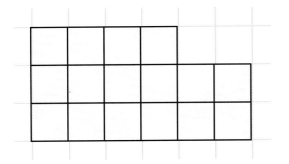

Hint: The shape has been drawn on cm² paper.

There are 18 one cm sides so the perimeter is 18 cm.

The shape covers 16 squares so the area is 16 cm².

Exercise 14A

1   These shapes are made of centimetre squares.
    Work out the perimeter and area of each shape:

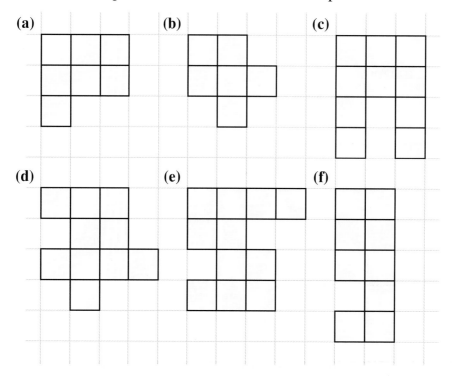

(a)   (b)   (c)

(d)   (e)   (f)

2   Each of these patios is made out of 1 m square slabs.
    Work out the perimeter and area of each.

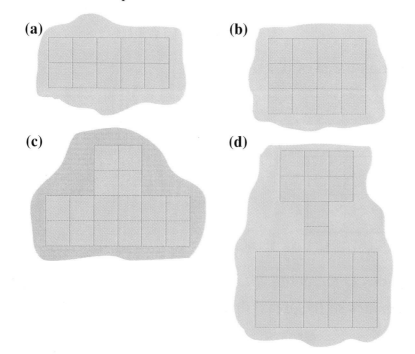

(a)   (b)

(c)   (d)

3   Asif has nine 1 cm² tiles.
He places them together to make this shape:

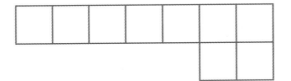

Its perimeter is 18 cm. Its area is 9 cm².
Place all of the 9 squares together to make at least
5 different shapes.
Record the perimeter and area of each shape and say
which has the smallest perimeter.

4   **(a)** What is the area of this shape made from
centimetre squares?

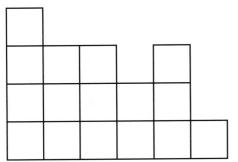

(b) Rearrange the tiles into a square.
(c) What is the perimeter of the square?

14.2 Perimeter and area of a rectangle

This rectangle is drawn on cm² paper:

The perimeter is:

   $4 + 4 + 3 + 3 = 14$ cm.

This is the same as:

   $(2 \times 4) + (2 \times 3) = 14$ cm.

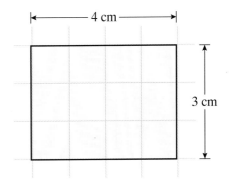

Remember to work
out the brackets first.
There is more about
this on page 206.

■   **For any rectangle:**
   Perimeter of rectangle is (2 × length) + (2 × width).

Example 2

Work out the perimeter of this rectangle:

Perimeter = 2 × length + 2 × width
= 2 × 5 + 2 × 3
= 16 cm.

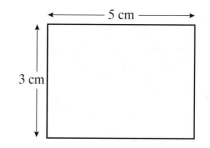

Exercise 14B

1 Work out the perimeter of these rectangles:

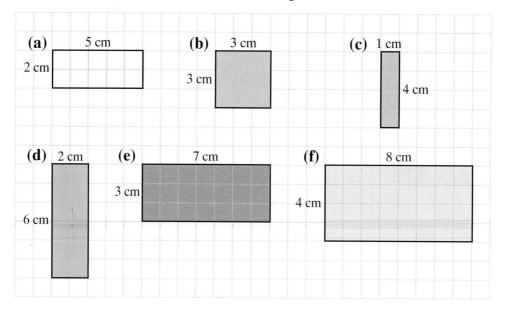

The area of a rectangle

This rectangle is made from 10 centimetre squares.

You can split the rectangle up... ...into two rows of five squares each.

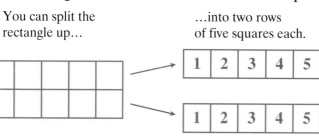

There are 2 lots of 5 squares so the area is:
2 × 5 = 10 cm²

■ **For any rectangle:**

Area of rectangle is length × width

Example 3

What is the area of this rectangular carpet?

The length is 5 metres.
The width is 4 metres.

Area = length × width, so
area = 5×4
     = $20\,\text{m}^2$

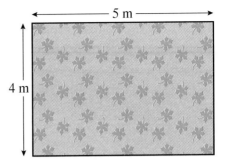

Exercise 14C

1 Work out the areas of these rectangles.

Make sure you give the units in your answers

(a) 5 cm / 3 cm

(b) 2 cm / 4 cm

(c) 1 cm / 5 cm

(d) 6 m / 4 m

(e) 10 m / 2 m

(f) 5 cm / 5 cm

Example 4

Russell's driveway measures 10 m by 3 m.
Work out its perimeter and area.

Perimeter of a rectangle = 2 × length + 2 × width
                        = $2 \times 10 + 2 \times 3$
                        = $20 + 6$
                        = $26\,\text{m}$

Area of a rectangle = length × width
                    = 10×3
                    = $30\,\text{m}^2$

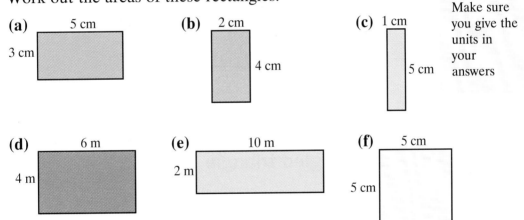

Exercise 14D

1   Use the formulae to work out the perimeter and area
of each of these rectangles:

(a)

8 cm

3 cm

(b)

10 cm

2 cm

(c)

4 cm

7 cm

(d)

6 m

6 m

(e)

10 m

5 m

(f)

12 cm

8 cm

14.3 Area of a right-angled triangle

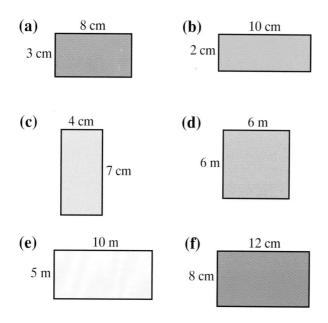

4 cm

3 cm

The area of this rectangle
is length × width.
$4 \times 3 = 12 \text{ cm}^2$.

If you draw in the diagonal
you create two identical
right-angled triangles.

The area of each triangle
is half the area of the
rectangle.

So the area of the blue triangle is:

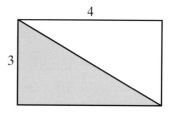

4

3

$\frac{1}{2}$ the area of the rectangle $= \frac{1}{2}$ of 4×3

$= \frac{1}{2}$ of 12

$= 6 \text{ cm}^2$.

Example 5

Work out the area of this triangle:

The area of the dotted rectangle is

Length $\times$ width $= 5 \times 4$
$= 20 \, \text{cm}^2.$

The area of the triangle is half the area of the rectangle:

area of triangle $= \frac{1}{2}$ of $20 \, \text{cm}^2$
$= 10 \, \text{cm}^2.$

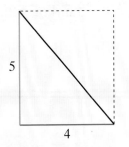

5

4

In this triangle the red side is the **base** and the blue side is the **height**.

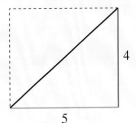

4

5

If you draw it this way the red side is the height and the blue side is the base.

- ■ **Area of a right-angled triangle is $\frac{1}{2}$ the area of the surrounding rectangle.**
- ■ **Area of a right-angled triangle is $\frac{1}{2}$ of base $\times$ height.**

Example 6

Work out the area of this triangle:

Area $= \frac{1}{2}$ of 4×10
$= \frac{1}{2}$ of 40
$= 20 \, \text{cm}^2$

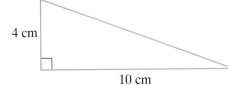

4 cm

10 cm

Exercise 14E

1   Work out the area of each of these triangles:

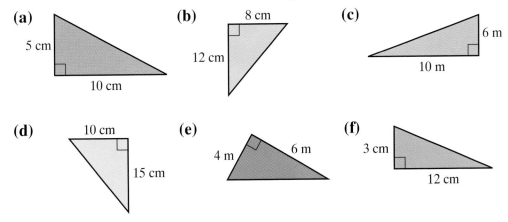

(a)

5 cm

10 cm

(b)

8 cm

12 cm

(c)

6 m

10 m

(d)

10 cm

15 cm

(e)

4 m

6 m

(f)

3 cm

12 cm

2 This building plot is in the shape of a right-angled triangle.
What is the area of the plot?

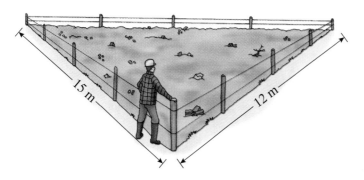

3 Work out the perimeter and area of this triangle:
What do you notice about your results?

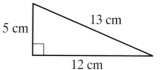

4 Which has the larger area:
(a) a right-angled triangle with base 9 cm and height 6 cm, or
(b) a rectangle with length 7 cm and width 4 cm?

14.4 Composite shapes

A shape made up from other shapes is called a **composite** shape.

■ **You can find the area of a composite shape by breaking it into simpler shapes.**

Example 7

Work out the area of this shape:

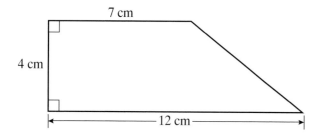

Break it into simpler shapes:

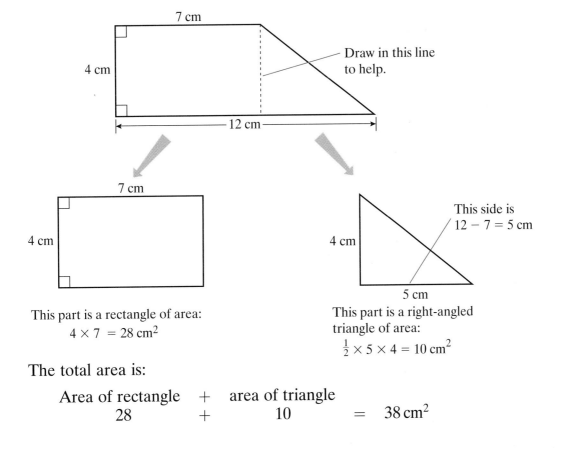

This part is a rectangle of area:
$4 \times 7 = 28 \text{ cm}^2$

This part is a right-angled triangle of area:
$\frac{1}{2} \times 5 \times 4 = 10 \text{ cm}^2$

The total area is:

Area of rectangle + area of triangle
28   +   10   = 38 cm^2

Exercise 14F

1   Work out the area of each of these composite shapes:

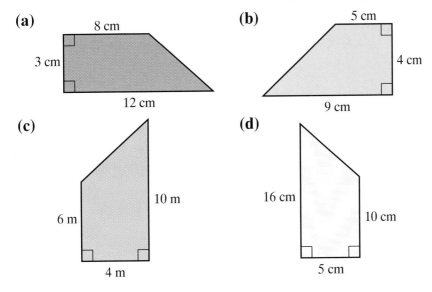

14.5 Curved-sided shapes

This section shows you how to estimate the area of a shape with curved sides.

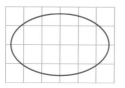

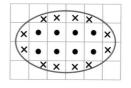

You cannot count the cm squares exactly to find the area of this shape.

Mark each whole square with a dot and each part square with a cross.

You can estimate the area of this shape by counting the dots and crosses.

Each dot counts as a whole square:

$\qquad$ 8 dots $= 8\,\text{cm}^2$.

Each cross counts as half a square:

$\qquad$ 12 crosses $= \frac{1}{2} \times 12$

$\qquad\qquad\qquad\quad = 6\,\text{cm}^2$

The estimate for the area of the shape is:

$\qquad$ Area of dots $+ \frac{1}{2} \times$ area of crosses $= 8 + 6 = 14\,\text{cm}^2$.

■ **To estimate the area of a shape with curved sides:**
$\qquad$ **area $\approx$ number of whole squares $+$ half of the number**
$\qquad\qquad$ **of part squares**

Hint:
$\approx$ means 'approximately equal to'.

Example 8

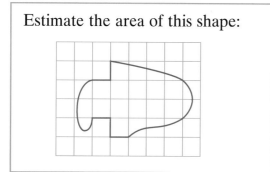

Estimate the area of this shape:

Mark in the dots and crosses:

There are 11 whole squares.

There are 12 part squares.

Area is $11 + \frac{1}{2}$ of $12 = 11 + 6 = 17$ squares.

Exercise 14G

1   Estimate the area for each of these shapes:

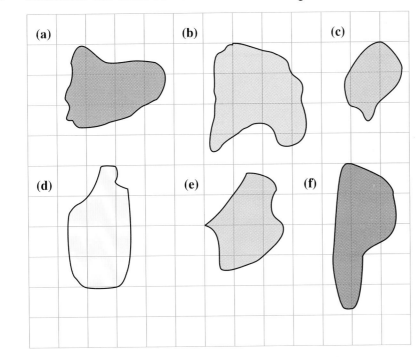

Hint:
All of the shapes on this page are drawn on cm² paper.

2   Use the dots and crosses method to estimate the areas of these shapes:

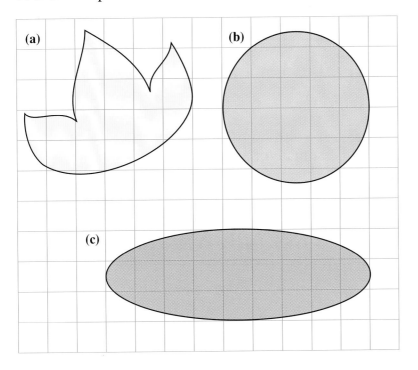

3   Copy and complete the table for each circle and square:

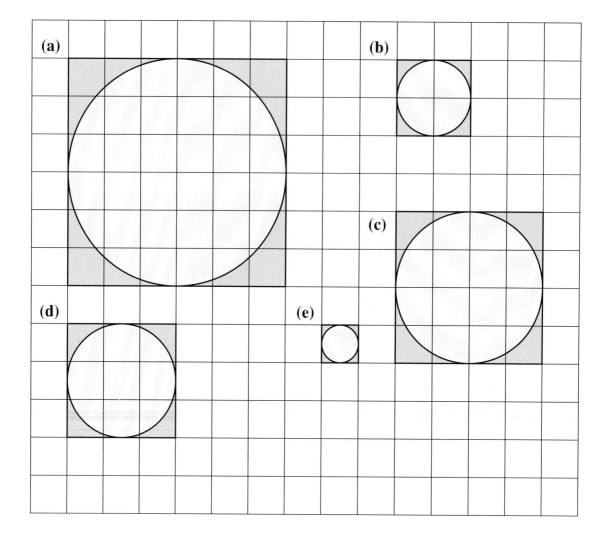

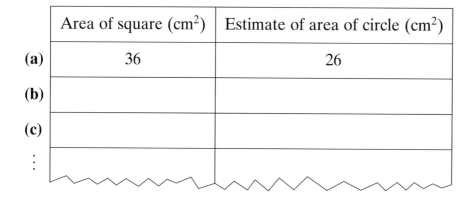

	Area of square (cm^2)	Estimate of area of circle (cm^2)
(a)	36	26
(b)		
(c)		
⋮		

14.6 Volume

Solid and hollow shapes take up space in three dimensions. The space that a three-dimensional shape takes up is called it's **volume**.

You can find the volume of this solid by counting how many cubes there are:

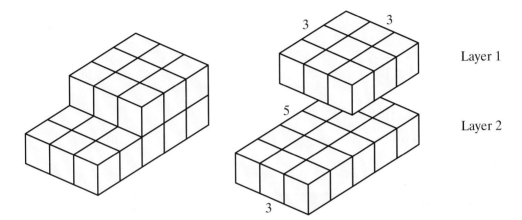

Layer 1

Layer 2

Split the shape into two layers to help you. There are:

$3 \times 3 = 9$ cubes in the top layer

$3 \times 5 = 15$ cubes in the bottom layer

So the volume is $9 + 15 = 24 \, \text{cm}^3$

■ **You can find the volume of some shapes by counting cubes.**

Example 9

Find the volume of this shape in cm^3:

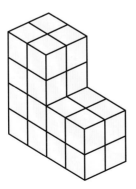

Think of the shape like this ...   ... or like this

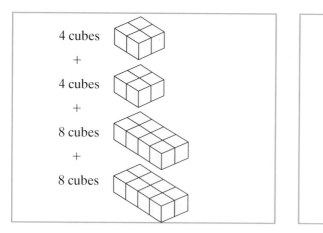

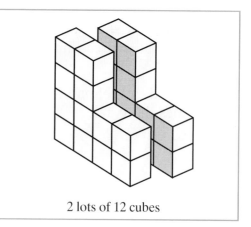

2 lots of 12 cubes

Counting the cubes, there are 24 in total.

The volume of the shape is 24 cm³.

Exercise 14H

1   Find the volume of these shapes. They are all made
    from centimetre cubes.

(a)   (b)   (c)   (d)

(e)   (f)

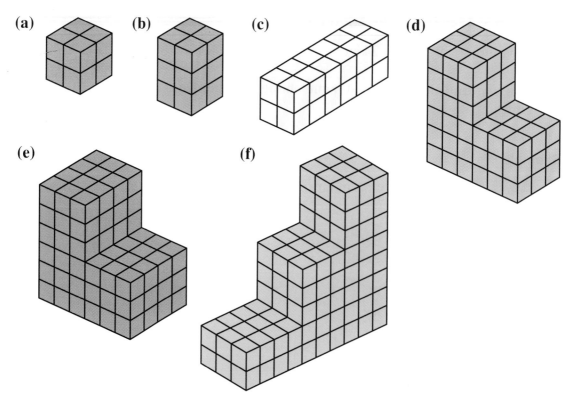

14.7 Volume of a cuboid

A shape with six rectangular faces is called a **cuboid**.

To find the volume of this cuboid:

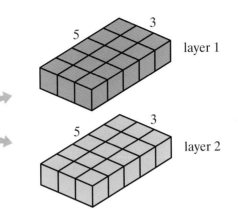

layer 1

layer 2

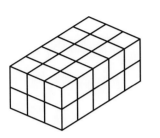

Count the cubes. There are 30 so the volume is 30 cm³.

Imagine the cuboid as two layers with $5 \times 3 = 15$ cubes in each.

There are 2 layers of 5×3 cubes so the volume is $2 \times 5 \times 3 = 30$ cm³.

Note that $2 \times 5 \times 3$ is the length × width × height.

For any cuboid:

■ **Volume of a cuboid is length × width × height.**

Example 10

Find the volume of this cuboid:

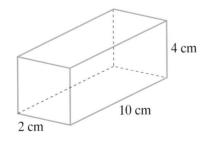

4 cm

10 cm

2 cm

Volume = length × width × height

$= 10 \times 2 \times 4$

$= 80$

So the volume is 80 cm³

Exercise 14I

1 Work out the volume of these cuboids:

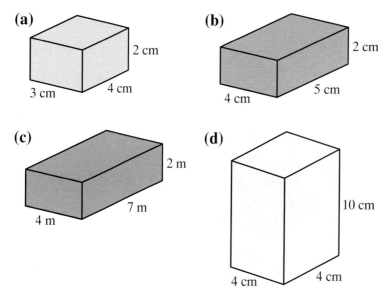

(a) 2 cm, 4 cm, 3 cm

(b) 2 cm, 5 cm, 4 cm

(c) 2 m, 7 m, 4 m

(d) 10 cm, 4 cm, 4 cm

2 Copy and complete this table showing volumes of cuboids:

Length (cm)	Width (cm)	Height (cm)	Volume (cm³)
5	2	4	
10	3	5	
6	2	3	
4	4	4	
8	5	3	
6	4	5	

Summary of key points

1 The distance around a flat shape is called the perimeter.

2 The amount of space that a shape covers is called its area.

3 The perimeter of a rectangle is
$2 \times$ length $+ 2 \times$ width.

4 The area of a rectangle is length $\times$ width.

5 Area of a right-angled triangle is $\frac{1}{2}$ of base $\times$ height.

6 You can find the area of a composite shape by breaking it down into more simple shapes.

7 To estimate the area of a shape with curved sides, add the number of whole squares to half the number of part squares.

8 You can find the volume of some shapes by counting cubes.

9 The volume of a cuboid is length $\times$ width $\times$ height.

15 Averages

Look at the way we use the word 'average':

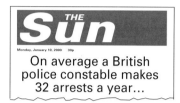

On average a British police constable makes 32 arrests a year...

The average temperature in July has risen by 2°C in the last 3 years.

The band, *Sound FX*, sell an average of 25 000 CD's a day!!

In these examples the word average means that something is typical.

An average is a useful way of comparing information as it allows all the data to be represented by a single value.

This chapter shows you how to work out three different averages.

15.1 The mode

■ **The mode of a set of data is the value which occurs most often.**

Brown is the most common eye colour

Example 1

Nine friends compared the number of books they bought in one year:

   4 6 8 4 7 3 5 4 4

The number 4 occurs most often.
So the mode is 4 books.

You can also say the modal number of books is 4.

Mode facts:
- There can be more than 1 mode.
- The mode does not have to be a number.
- Sometimes there is no mode.

Example 2

These numbers show how often a group of children visited Charlwood Towers theme park in one month:

Levi went three times

1, 0, 2, 1, 0, 3, 0, 2, 1, 5

Ben went twice

Find the mode for the data.

There are two modes: 0 and 1
They both appear three times.

Data which has two modes is also called **bi-modal**.

Example 3

This table shows the colour of 10 cars.

Ford	VW	Ford	Seat	Rover	VW	Citroen	Rover	Ford	BMW
green	blue	red	blue	white	black	green	blue	red	black

Find: **(a)** the modal make of car
      (b) the modal colour of car.

(a) The modal make of car is Ford.
(b) The modal colour is blue.

Notice that the mode is not a number.

Example 4

The list shows the house numbers of twelve children:

2, 6, 4, 79, 36, 15, 23, 98, 101, 31, 253, 64

Find the mode.

All the numbers appear only once so there is no mode.

This data has no mode.

Exercise 15A

1   This list shows the number of students that used the internet in one week:

Mon	Tues	Wed	Thurs	Fri
24	35	40	35	29

What is the mode of this data?

2 Joe's scores for different subjects are shown below.

Write down the modal score for each subject.

Maths	6	8	5	6	8	3	5	6	9	10	8
English	12	12	11	8	7	8	11	5	8	10	
History	23	24	15	23	36	18	25	36	23		
French	3	5	7	9	3	5	3	10	9	6	

3 Here are some test results:

Class A	6	3	10	10	7	7	6	5	8	7	4	7	10	3	1			
Class B	1	8	3	9	4	8	1	3	8	8	4	6	8	8	5	4	2	1

(a) Work out the modal mark for each class.
(b) Which class had the largest mode?

4 The shoe sizes of the pupils in 8C are:

6, 7, 6, 5, 8, 13, 10, 3, 5, 6, 8, 3, 8, 5, 6,
9, 10, 4, 5, 6, 3, 6, 12, 6, 4, 6, 9, 7, 10, 6.

Find the modal shoe size.

5 This list shows how many letters were delivered to one street on each day in February:

2, 6, 8, 4, 6, 4, 3, 2, 8, 2, 0, 1, 0, 3,
2, 3, 4, 3, 7, 5, 1, 8, 6, 0, 3, 3, 5, 3

Work out the mode.

15.2 Using a table or chart to find the mode

In a frequency table the mode is the value with the highest frequency.

Example 5

Rashida throws a pair of dice 36 times and she records her scores.

2	4	7	9	10	8	7	8	7
6	7	10	7	9	3	4	5	5
12	6	6	10	9	8	8	4	5
6	11	5	6	5	3	7	7	7

She completes a frequency table.

Score	Tally	Frequency
2	$\vert$	1
3	$\vert\vert$	2
4	$\vert\vert\vert$	3
5	$\cancel{\vert\vert\vert\vert}$	5
6	$\cancel{\vert\vert\vert\vert}$	5
7	$\cancel{\vert\vert\vert\vert}\ \vert\vert\vert$	8
8	$\vert\vert\vert\vert$	4
9	$\vert\vert\vert$	3
10	$\vert\vert\vert$	3
11	$\vert$	1
12	$\vert$	1

The score which occurs the most has the highest frequency.

So Rashida's mode is a score of 7.

■ **In a frequency table, the mode is the value with the highest frequency.**

It is easy to find the mode from a bar chart.

Example 6

This bar chart shows how many cars each household in a small village has:

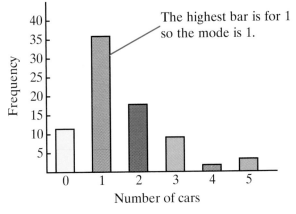

The highest bar is for 1 so the mode is 1.

■ **In a bar chart the mode is the value with the highest bar.**

Exercise 15B

1   This table shows how long flights were delayed at Birmingham airport one day:

No. of hours late	0	1	2	3	4
Frequency	10	12	6	2	1

Hint: Look for the number of hours with the highest frequency.

Work out the mode for the number of hours late.

2   The number of strikes Mike made in 58 games of ten pin bowling are:

> 0, 3, 5, 3, 2, 6, 4, 2, 4, 5, 8, 3, 2, 1, 0, 2, 5, 3,
> 5, 3, 6, 3, 5, 2, 1, 4, 3, 3, 6, 3, 9, 9, 3, 5, 2, 5,
> 1, 6, 4, 3, 7, 3, 2, 4, 5, 3, 7, 1, 7, 3, 4, 3, 7, 6,
> 0, 3, 7, 5

(a) Use the data to copy and complete the following frequency table.

(b) Work out the mode.

no. of strikes	tally	frequency
0		
1		
2		
3		
4		
5		
6		
7		
8		
9		

3 This bar chart shows the number of goals a netball team scored per match in one season.

Write down the modal number of goals scored.

5 Yen records the shoe size for the pupils in her class. She draws a bar chart to show her results.

(a) Write down the two modes.
(b) Give a reason why you think there may be two modes.

15.3 The median

■ **The median is the middle value when the data is arranged in order of size**

Example 7

The heights of five girls are:

Candice 150 cm,   Marie 154 cm,   Rashida 140 cm,
Georgina 155 cm,   Sarah 175 cm.

To find the median height, arrange the heights in order and find the middle value:

140   150   154   155   175

↑
middle value

The median height is 154 cm.

Example 8

The number of goals Amy scores in nine hockey games are:

2, 1, 0, 1, 0, 3, 2, 1, 0

Work out her median score.

Arrange the scores in order:

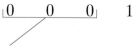 0   0   0   1   1   1   2   2   3

There were
no goals in
three games

The median is the
middle value: 1 goal

Remember to write
each score down the
correct number of
times.

Example 9

This list shows the number of days it rained each month in one year.

Month	Jan	Feb	Mar	Apr	May	Jun	Jul	Aug	Sept	Oct	Nov	Dec
No. of days	12	9	15	12	8	4	7	5	10	12	8	11

Find the median number of rainy days.

First arrange the numbers in order:

4 5 7 8 8 ⑨ ⑩ 11 12 12 12 15

Remember to write 8 twice and 12 three times.

There are two middle values so add them together and divide by two.

The median is $\dfrac{(9 + 10)}{2}$ or $9\frac{1}{2}$ days.

■ **If there is an even number of values then you find the median by adding the middle two values and dividing by 2.**

Exercise 15C

1 Arrange the following sets of data in order and find the median:

(a) 2, 4, 6, 7, 9

(b) £1, £8, £9, £2, £5, £1, £1

(c) 12 kg, 16 kg, 10 kg, 8 kg, 10 kg, 9 kg, 14 kg, 20 kg

2 Theo completes three tests in Maths, Science and English. His marks for each question are:

Maths	2	4	8	1	0	3	12	3	5	2	1	3	0	2	4
Science	12	15	9	12	13	2	5	10							
English	21	33	15												

(a) Work out the median mark for each subject.

(b) Which subject had the largest median?

3 Rashid counts the number of cars which pass by his school every five minutes during a lesson.

12 8 10 5 6 3 2 9 12 7 3 2

Work out the median.

4 Daphne throws a dice 15 times. Here are her results:

3, 2, 6, 3, 1, 4, 3, 5, 2, 1, 6, 3, 2, 5, 1

(a) Calculate the median.

(b) Work out the mode.

5 The graph below shows the number of books borrowed from the school library during the week.

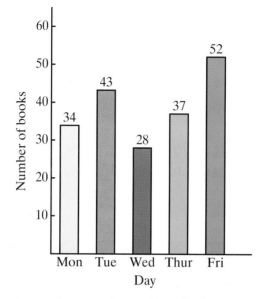

(a) Write down the number of books borrowed for each day.

(b) Work out the median number of books borrowed.

6 The graph below shows the test scores for seven of the pupils in class 2H.

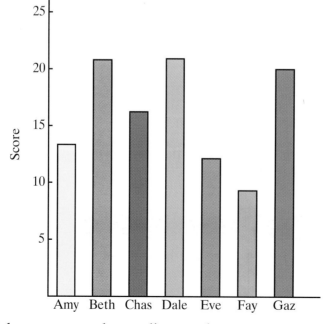

Which person got the median mark.

15.4 The mean

The mean is the sum of all the values divided by the number of values.

■ **Mean** $= \dfrac{\textbf{sum of values}}{\textbf{number of values}}$

Example 10

The number of vegetarian meals served on six UKAir flights is:

  6, 13, 4, 8, 5, 12

Calculate the mean number of vegetarian meals on a UKAir flight.

Add the values ...

  $6 + 13 + 4 + 8 + 5 + 12 = 48$

... and divide by the number of values:

  $48 \div 6 = 8$

So the mean is 8 vegetarian meals.

For Virgo Atlantic the number of vegetarian meals on five flights is:

  7, 10, 6, 15, 9

Add the values ...

  $= 7 + 10 + 6 + 15 + 9 = 47$

... and divide by the number of values:

  $47 \div 5 = 9.4$

So the mean is 9.4 vegetarian meals.

 Page 260 shows you how to use your calculator to work out averages.

The mean does not have to be a whole number.

Exercise 15D

1 Find the mean for these sets of data:
   (a) 2, 4, 6, 7, 9, 12, 15, 19
   (b) £1, £8, £9, £2, £5, £1, £1, £3, £4
   (c) 12 kg, 16 kg, 10 kg, 8 kg, 10 kg, 9 kg, 14 kg, 20 kg

2 Kate takes three tests in Maths, Science and English.
Her marks for the questions in the tests are:

Maths	2	4	8	1	0	3	12	6	5	2	1	3	0	3	4
Science	12	15	9	12	13	2	5	10	13	15					
English	21	33	15	24	36	45									

Work out the mean mark for each of the subjects.

3 Levi scores 124 runs in eight innings.
Work out her average number of runs per innings.

4 Nassar buys 10 packs of sweets.
The mean number of sweets per packet is 12.
Work out the total number of sweets Nassar buys.

Hint: Work out how many days there are in five weeks.

5 Shanise's website is visited 2170 times in five weeks.
What is the mean number of hits per day?

15.5 The range

The range of a set of data tells you how spread out the data is.

In maths the range is the difference between the highest and lowest value in your data.

■ **range = highest value − lowest value**

Example 11

The number of points scored by a rugby team in ten games is:

12, 34, 56, 45, 26, 17, 5, 9, 23, 31

Calculate the range of points scored.

The highest score was 56 and the lowest was 5 so:

range = 56 − 5 = 51 points

Exercise 15E

1 Find the range for each set of data:
  (a) 2, 4, 6, 7, 9, 12, 15, 19
  (b) £1, £8, £9, £2, £5, £1, £1, £3, £4
  (c) 12 kg, 16 kg, 10 kg, 8 kg, 10 kg, 9 kg, 14 kg, 20 kg

2 Jon did 12 English homeworks. His highest mark was 18 and his lowest mark was 11. What was Jon's range of marks?

3 The smallest value in a set of data is 9 and the range is 12. What is the highest number?

4 This table shows the lowest temperature on each day in one week:

Day	Mon	Tue	Wed	Thu	Fri	Sat	Sun
Temp. (°C)	2	3	6	1	0	−3	−5

What is the range of the temperatures?

Exercise 15F

Work out the mode, median and mean for each set of data.

1 (a) 5, 3, 5, 12, 7, 5, 1, 8, 9, 10
(b) £12, £32, £15, £12, £30, £25, £30, £12
(c) 1.8, 2.3, 5.6, 1.8, 3.5, 2.3, 4.5, 1.9, 2.7, 4.1, 5.2, 3.6, 2.3, 4.5, 3.6

2 This table shows how many cars Ray sells each month.

Month	Jan	Feb	Mar	Apr	May	Jun	Jul	Aug	Sept	Oct	Nov	Dec
No. of sales	8	12	23	15	20	12	25	12	21	18	15	12

(a) Calculate the mean.
(b) Calculate the median.
(c) Calculate the mode.
(d) Calculate the range.

3 Dianne throws a pair of dice 25 times. She adds up the numbers on both dice. Her scores are:

2, 7, 6, 8, 9, 10, 8, 4, 3, 11, 12, 9, 10, 6, 7, 8, 10, 11, 3, 2, 5, 8, 6, 9, 12

(a) Calculate the mean.
(b) Calculate the median.
(c) Calculate the mode.
(d) Calculate the range.

4 This list shows how many eggs were found in 50 nests:

2	3	6	4	5	6	4	3	4	3
2	1	2	5	3	4	5	2	2	4
3	5	5	2	3	3	4	4	5	3
5	4	6	3	2	4	4	2	4	3
2	4	2	5	3	1	3	4	2	2

(a) Copy and complete this frequency table:

no. of eggs	tally	frequency	no. of eggs × frequency

(b) Calculate the mean.
(c) Write down the mode.
(c) Work out the range.

15.6 Comparing data

You can use averages to compare different sets of data.

■ **To compare data fairly you should look at the average (mean, mode or median) value AND the range (spread) of the values**

Example 12

Emma and Lucy compared their science homework marks.

	Wk 1	Wk 2	Wk 3	Wk 4	Wk 5	Wk 6	Wk 7	Wk 8	Wk 9	Wk 10
Emma	3	8	1	8	9	2	9	8	4	8
Lucy	6	7	7	6	6	6	7	6	6	6

The mean marks are:

Emma: mean $= \dfrac{3+8+1+8+9+2+9+8+4+8}{10} = \dfrac{60}{10} = 6$

Lucy: mean $= \dfrac{6+7+7+6+6+6+7+6+6+6}{10} = \dfrac{63}{10} = 6.3$

So Lucy's mean mark is higher than Emma's.

The range of Emma's marks is:

range $=$ highest mark $-$ lowest mark $= 9 - 1 = 8$

and Lucy's range of marks is:

range $=$ highest mark $-$ lowest mark $= 7 - 6 = 1$

Lucy's range is lower. Her marks are less spread out.

Emma has some high marks but also some low ones. Her marks are more spread out.

Overall, it is Lucy who did better.

Exercise 15G

1 Sam and his brother Jim play cricket.
   In ten innings the numbers of runs they scored are:

Sam	36	33	38	44	40	39	42	37	31	45
Jim	8	57	14	0	12	46	64	51	48	50

   (a) Work out:
      (i) the mean number of runs they each scored.
      (ii) the range of their scores.
   (b) Comment, with reasons, on who did best in these ten innings.

2 Anton and Dominic have both done 10 history homeworks.
   Anton's marks are:

   8 1 7 9 8 8 0 2 9 8

   Dominic's marks had a mean of 6.5 and a range of 1.
   (a) Work out:
      • the mean, median and mode of Anton's marks
      • the range of Anton's marks
   (b) Comment on which friend might have done best.

Summary of key points

1 The mode of a set of data is the value which occurs most often.

2 In a frequency table, the mode is the value with the highest frequency.

3 In a bar chart the mode is the value with the highest bar.

4 The median is the middle value when the data is arranged in order of size.

5 If there is an even number of values then the median is worked out by adding the middle two values and dividing by 2.

6 $\text{Mean} = \dfrac{\text{sum of values}}{\text{number of values}}$

7 range = highest value − lowest value

8 To compare data fairly you should look at the average (mean, mode or median) value AND the range (spread) of the values.

16 Using and applying mathematics

In this chapter you will learn about the process behind doing a mathematical investigation.

This is the problem that you will be investigating:

Shaking hands

Andrea has a birthday party:

She asks each of her friends to shake hands with everyone else just once.

Investigate to find the relationship between the number of friends and the number of handshakes.

The first step is to:

Understand the problem

The best way to understand the problem is to just have a go. Suppose Andrea has invited four friends: Bronwen, Charlie, Dipesh and Elaine.

Five of the possible handshakes could be:

    Andrea and Bronwen
    Andrea and Charlie
    Andrea and Dipesh
    Andrea and Elaine
    Bronwen and Charlie

Exercise 16A

1   Find the other five handshakes to show that there are ten possible handshakes when there are four friends.

Make the problem as simple as you can

To help you understand the problem, try out the simplest cases first.

Example 1

How many handshakes will there be if Andrea invites one friend, Bronwen?

There will be one handshake:

> Andrea and Bronwen

Example 2

How many handshakes will there be if Andrea invites Charlie as well, so there are two friends?

The handshakes will be:

> Andrea and Bronwen
> Andrea and Charlie
> Bronwen and Charlie

So there will be three handshakes if Andrea invites two friends

Exercise 16B

1   List all the handshakes if Andrea invites three friends: Bronwen, Charlie and Dipesh.

    How many handshakes are there with three friends?

Plan and use a strategy

A strategy is an ordered approach to a problem.

Imagine trying to work out how many handshakes there would be at this party!

Using a strategy will mean that you don't miss any handshakes.

Example 3

How many handshakes will there be if Andrea invites five friends: Bronwen, Charlie, Dipesh, Elaine and Flora?

The strategy will be:

Count all of Andrea's handshakes first.
Then count all of Bronwen's.
Then count all of Charlie's.
And so on . . .
To save time just use the first letter of each name:
AF = Andrea and Flora
The handshakes for each person are:

Andrea:	AB	AC	AD	AE	AF	5
Bronwen:	BC	BD	BE	BF		4
Charlie:	CD	CE	CF			3
Dipesh:	DE	DF				2
Elaine:	EF					1

Hint:
You don't need to do BA as Bronwen has already shaken hands with Andrea.

Flora has already shaken hands with everyone.

So the number of handshakes for 5 friends is:

$$5 + 4 + 3 + 2 + 1 = 15$$

Exercise 16C

1   (a) Use this strategy to check the results so far:

Number of friends:	1	2	3	4	5
Number of handshakes:	1	3	6	10	15

(b) Use the strategy to show that there will be 21 handshakes if Andrea invites a sixth friend, Graham.

Record your results

Once you have started to get some results it is best to
record them in a table.

Exercise 16D

1   Copy and complete this table:

Number of friends	Number of handshakes
1	1
2	3
3	6
6	

Always make sure
your tables are clearly
labelled.

Make predictions

Once you have your results in a table you should
see if you can find any patterns.

A simple pattern to see here is that the number of
handshakes grows as the number of friends grows.

The number of handshakes also follows a pattern:

1	3	6	10	15	21
odd	odd	even	even	odd	odd

which is not so obvious.

You can use your observations to make **predictions**.

Example 4

Predict whether the number of handshakes will be odd or
even for seven friends.

The results so far are:

Number of friends	Number of handshakes	Odd or even
1	1	odd
2	3	odd
3	6	even
4	10	even
5	15	odd
6	21	odd
7		even

Even though you don't know the number of handshakes you can predict that it will be an even number.

Exercise 16E

1　Predict whether there will be an odd or even number when there are:

(a) 10 friends 　　**(b)** 20 friends 　　**(c)** 50 friends

Show how you get your answers.

A good way to find patterns in number sequences is to use **differences**. You can see a pattern in your results if you find the difference between each pair of numbers.

Number of friends	1	2	3	4	5	6
Number of handshakes	1	3	6	10	15	21

$$+2 \quad +3 \quad +4 \quad +5 \quad +6$$

The number of handshakes increases by a simple pattern　2, 3, 4, 5, 6, . . .

You can use this to predict that for 7 friends there will be　$21 + 7 = 28$ handshakes.

Example 5

How many handshakes will there be for 8 friends?

Use the pattern to make a prediction:

```
  +2   +3    +4    +5    +6    +7    +8
1    3    6    10    15    21    28    36 handshakes
```

If you know the pattern and the first answer you can find the answer without drawing out the whole table each time.

Exercise 16F

1   Use a pattern to predict how many handshakes there will be for:

   (a) 8 friends   **(b)** 9 friends   **(c)** 10 friends

Testing predictions

Whenever you make a prediction you should test it to check whether it is a good one.

Example 6

Test the prediction that there will be 28 handshakes if Andrea invites 7 friends.

Use the strategy to count the handshakes.

Andrea:	AB	AC	AD	AE	AF	AG	AH
Bronwen:	BC	BD	BE	BF	BG	BH	
Charlie:	CD	CE	CF	CG	CH		
Dipesh:	DE	DF	DG	DH			
Elaine:	EF	EG	EH				
Flora:	FG	FH					
Graham:	GH						

Herbert has already shaken hands with everyone.

There are 28 pairs of letters so there are 28 handshakes when Andrea invites 7 friends.
The prediction was a good one!

Exercise 16G

1 Using the strategy, test the predictions that you made for:

   (a) 8 friends   **(b)** 9 friends   **(c)** 10 friends

Summary

The steps you should take in any mathematical investigation are:

- Understand the problem – have a go.
- Make the problem as simple as you can.
- Use an ordered approach – plan a strategy.
- Record your results – make a table.
- Make predictions.
- Test your predictions.

17 Calculators and computers

This chapter shows you how to use scientific calculators, graphical calculators and computer software to help build on and extend the work you have been studying in the other chapters of this book.

The examples will work on Casio calculators, the spreadsheet examples are based on Microsoft Excel and the examples for drawing angles, polygons and triangles work with WinLogo.

17.1 Using your square root key

You can find square roots using the $\sqrt{}$ key.

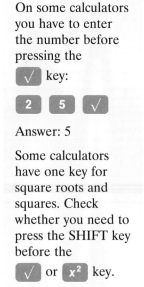

On some calculators you have to enter the number before pressing the $\sqrt{}$ key:

⟦2⟧ ⟦5⟧ ⟦√⟧

Answer: 5

Some calculators have one key for square roots and squares. Check whether you need to press the SHIFT key before the $\sqrt{}$ or x^2 key.

Get to know your calculator!

Example 1

Find:

(a) $\sqrt{25}$　　(b) $\sqrt{4} + \sqrt{9}$　　(c) $\sqrt{(3^2 + 4^2)}$

(a) Press ⟦√⟧ ⟦2⟧ ⟦5⟧ ⟦=⟧

　　Answer: 5

(b) Press ⟦√⟧ ⟦4⟧ ⟦+⟧ ⟦√⟧ ⟦9⟧ ⟦=⟧

　　Answer: 5

(c) Press ⟦√⟧ ⟦[(...⟧ ⟦3⟧ ⟦x²⟧ ⟦+⟧ ⟦4⟧ ⟦x²⟧ ⟦...)]⟧ ⟦=⟧

　　Answer: 5

Exercise 17A

1　Calculate $\sqrt{324}$　　　　　　2　Calculate $\sqrt{1369}$

3　Calculate $\sqrt{576}$　　　　　　4　Calculate $\sqrt{2304} - \sqrt{289}$

5　Calculate $\sqrt{(6^2 + 8^2)}$　　　　6　Calculate $\sqrt{(5^2 + 12^2)}$

7　Calculate $\sqrt{25} + \sqrt{144}$　　　8　Calculate $\sqrt{441} \div \sqrt{49}$

9　Calculate $\sqrt{1521} \div \sqrt{169}$　　10　Calculate $\sqrt{(29^2 - 21^2)}$

11 Investigate what happens if you keep taking the square root starting with any 10 digit number?

Press the $\sqrt{}$ key, enter your 10 digit number, press

= , $\sqrt{}$, Ans ,

$\sqrt{}$, Ans , ...

12 Does:
(a) $\sqrt{(16 \times 25)} = \sqrt{16} \times \sqrt{25}$?
(b) $\sqrt{(36 + 64)} = \sqrt{36} + \sqrt{64}$?
(c) $\sqrt{(225 \div 25)} = \sqrt{225} \div \sqrt{25}$?
(d) $\sqrt{(100 - 36)} = \sqrt{100} - \sqrt{36}$?

17.2 Generating sequences

You can use a spreadsheet to generate sequences.

There is more on sequences on page 83.

Enter these numbers in row 1:

	A	B	C	D	E	F
1	1	2	1	3	5	1
2						
3						

Type in these formulae:

$= A1 + 1$ in cell A2
$= B1 + 2$ in cell B2
$= C1 + 2$ in cell C2
$= D1 + 3$ in cell D2
$= E1 + 5$ in cell E2
$= F1*2$ in cell A2

Highlight the numbers the formulae have produced in row 2 ...

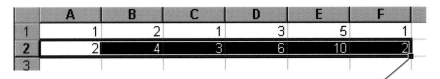

	A	B	C	D	E	F
1	1	2	1	3	5	1
2	2	4	3	6	10	2
3						

... and click and drag the black box down to row 12 to generate the sequences. Your spreadsheet should look like the one on the next page.

	A	B	C	D	E	F
1	1	2	1	3	5	1
2	2	4	3	6	10	2
3	3	5	5	9	15	4
4	4	6	7	12	20	8
5	5	7	9	15	25	16
6	6	8	11	18	30	32
7	7	9	13	21	35	64
8	8	10	15	24	40	128
9	9	11	17	27	45	256
10	10	12	19	30	50	512
11	11	13	21	33	55	1024
12	12	14	23	36	60	2048

The sequences show the first 12:

positive whole numbers in column A

even numbers in column B

odd numbers in column C

multiples of 3 in column D

multiples of 5 in column E

powers of 2 in column F.

Exercise 17B   Spreadsheet

1   Use a spreadsheet to generate the sequences shown below by entering the numbers in row 1 and a formula in row 2.

	A	B	C	D	E	F
1	4	10	10	5	0	1
2	8	20	9	4	-1	3
3	12	30	8	3	-2	9
4	16	40	7	2	-3	27
5	20	50	6	1	-4	81
6	24	60	5	0	-5	243
7	28	70	4	-1	-6	729
8	32	80	3	-2	-7	2187
9	36	90	2	-3	-8	6561
10	40	100	1	-4	-9	19683

Hints:

Column A shows the first 10 multiples of 4.

Column B shows the first 10 multiples of 10.

Each term in column C is one less than the previous term.

Columns D and E follow the same pattern as column C.

In column F each term is three times as large as the one before. These numbers are the first 10 powers of 3.

17.3 Percentages

Example 2

(a) Find 12% of £3500   **(b)** Find 9% of 8000 CDs
(c) Find 25% of 5056 kg

Press

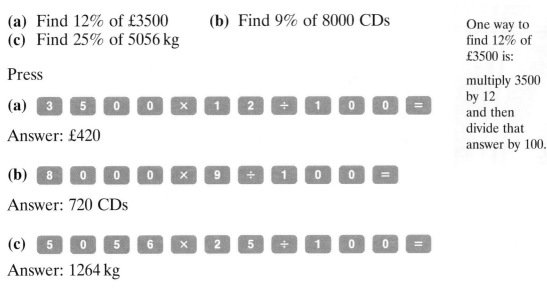

(a)
Answer: £420

(b)
Answer: 720 CDs

(c)
Answer: 1264 kg

One way to
find 12% of
£3500 is:

multiply 3500
by 12
and then
divide that
answer by 100.

Exercise 17C   Scientific calculator

1   **(a)** Calculate 15% of 2800 sweets
       (b) Calculate 30% of 60 pencils
       (c) Calculate 75% of 65 000 people

2   Last year Matthew weighed 65 kg. This year his weight
       has gone up by 4%. How many kilograms has Matthew
       put on?

3   Ali was earning £26 500 a year when he was given a
       pay increase of 3%. How much was his increase?

4   In the 1998/1999 soccer season the average home
       attendance for a team was 32 400. The following season
       this increased by 7%. How many more people is this?

5   Anna-Natasha put £6500 in a Building Society. After
       1 year she gained 6% interest. How much interest did
       Anna-Natasha receive?

Hints.
In question:
2 find 4% of 65
3 find 3% of 26 500
4 find 7% of 32 400
5 find 6% of 6500
6 find 9% of the
  total

6 Joshua went into his local games store and bought 2 light guns at £14.99 each, 5 CD-R games at £17.99 each, 1 dual shock analogue joy pad at £18.99 each, 6 memory cards at £10.95 each and 2 scart cables for £7.98 each.

  (a) What was Joshua's total bill?

  (b) Joshua was offered a discount of 9% off his bill. How much was his discount to the nearest penny?

17.4 Number machines

You can use a spreadsheet to find the output of a number machine.

There is more on number machines on page 76.

Example 3

This is a × 0.8 number machine:

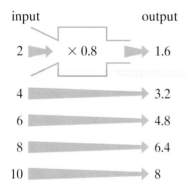

input		output
2	× 0.8	1.6
4		3.2
6		4.8
8		6.4
10		8

To produce the inputs and outputs above:

Enter 2 in cell A1 and the two formulae in cells A2 and B1.

	A	B
1	2	=A1*0.8
2	=A1+2	
3		
4		
5		

Copy down the formula in cell A2 to A5 and the formula in B1 to B5.

	A	B
1	2	=A1*0.8
2	=A1+2	=A2*0.8
3	=A2+2	=A3*0.8
4	=A3+2	=A4*0.8
5	=A4+2	=A5*0.8

This will produce the required Inputs and Outputs in column A and column B.

	A	B
1	2	1.6
2	4	3.2
3	6	4.8
4	8	6.4
5	10	8

Exercise 17D   Spreadsheet

Use a spreadsheet to find the output for these number machines:

1

input	rule	output
3	× 0.6	
6		
9		
12		
15		

2

input	rule	output
12	÷ 0.8	
10		
8		
6		
4		

3

input	rule	output
5	× 100	
10		
15		
20		
25		

4

input	rule	output
10000	÷ 10	
2000		
400		
80		
16		

Try and create the input column using a formula.

5

input	rule	output
5	+ 4.5	
25		
125		
625		
3125		

6

input	rule	output
10	−10	
5		
0		
–5		
–10		

7

input	rule	output
3	÷3 + 10	
9		
27		
81		
243		

8

input	rule	output
1	×4 − 3	
2		
4		
8		
16		

Hint:
7 and 8 are both two-step number machines.

17.5 Handling data

You can use a spreadsheet to calculate the mean, median, mode and range for given data. You can also produce charts to display the data.

There is more about averages on page 232.

Exercise 17E   Spreadsheet

1   Enter the following data in cells A1 to A11 on a spreadsheet.

	A
1	3
2	5
3	7
4	12
5	17
6	17
7	22
8	26
9	27
10	28
11	30

(a) In cell A12 enter =average (A1:A11) to calculate the mean of the data.

(b) In cell A13 enter =median (A1:A11) to calculate the median of the data.

(c) In cell A14 enter =mode (A1:A11) to calculate the mode of the data.

(d) In cell A15 enter =A11 − A1 to calculate the range of the data.

(e) Change the value of the data in cell A11 from 30 to 130.
   How does this affect the three averages?

(f) Which is the fairest average to use
   (i) before the change   (ii) after the change

2   (a) Use a spreadsheet to create a bar chart of the following maximum daily temperatures.

	A	B	C	D	E	F	G	H
1	Day	Sunday	Monday	Tuesday	Wednesday	Thursday	Friday	Saturday
2	Degrees Celsius, maximum	10	12	14	11	16	17	15

In Microsoft Excel highlight the cells B1, B2, . . ., H1,H2 and use the chart wizard to assist you.

Add a title, and label the axes when prompted.

In Excel, bar charts are called column charts!

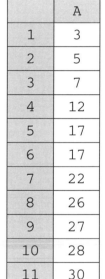

Click on the

button to start the chart wizard

(b) Enter the minimum temperatures into your spreadsheet in row 3 and create a second bar chart showing both the maximum and minimum bars side by side.

	A	B	C	D	E	F	G	H
1	Day	Sunday	Monday	Tuesday	Wednesday	Thursday	Friday	Saturday
2	Maximum temp. (°C)	10	12	14	11	16	17	15
3	Minimum temp. (°C)	4	6	7	6	8	9	7

(c) Highlight the days of the week together with the minimum temperatures and create a line graph similar to the one below.

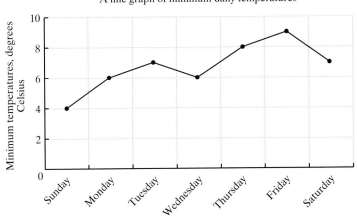

A line graph of minimum daily temperatures

Day of the week

In Excel, use the Ctrl key on your keyboard to highlight the two rows which are not next to each other.

(d) The following data was obtained on the World Wide Web and gives the winning time for the Men's and Women's 100 m sprint in the Olympic games from 1928 to 1996.

Year and Place	Men	Women
Amsterdam 1928	10.8	12.2
Los Angeles 1932	10.3	11.9
Berlin 1936	10.3	11.5
London 1948	10.3	11.9
Helsinki 1952	10.4	11.5
Melbourne 1956	10.5	11.5
Rome 1960	10.2	11.0
Tokyo 1964	10.0	11.4
Mexico City 1968	9.95	11.0
Munich 1972	10.14	11.0
Montreal 1976	10.06	11.0
Moscow 1980	10.25	11.0
Los Angeles 1984	9.99	10.9
Seoul 1988	9.92	10.5
Barcelona 1992	9.96	10.8
Atlanta 1996	9.84	10.94

Use a spreadsheet to:
(i) calculate the mean time for both the Men's and Women's sprint
(ii) draw line graphs comparing Men's and Women's results.

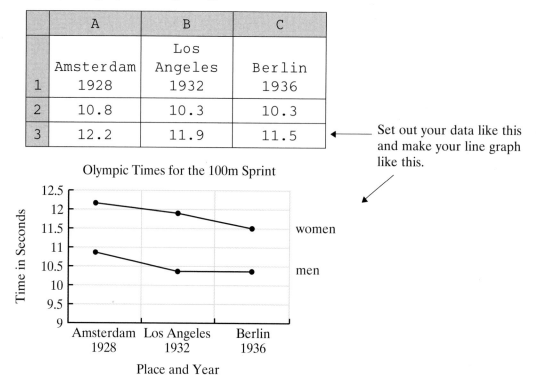

	A	B	C
1	Amsterdam 1928	Los Angeles 1932	Berlin 1936
2	10.8	10.3	10.3
3	12.2	11.9	11.5

Set out your data like this and make your line graph like this.

Olympic Times for the 100m Sprint

17.6 Angles and polygons

It is possible to draw angles, triangles and polygons on a computer using the program WinLogo.

Commander

rt 90

Type your instructions here and then press the Enter key before typing your next instruction.

In WinLogo you must provide instructions to move the 'turtle' around the screen.

The turtle begins this way round

rt 90
will turn it 90°
clockwise

fd 100
will move it forward
'100' places and
draw a line '100'
units long

Example 4

Draw on screen:

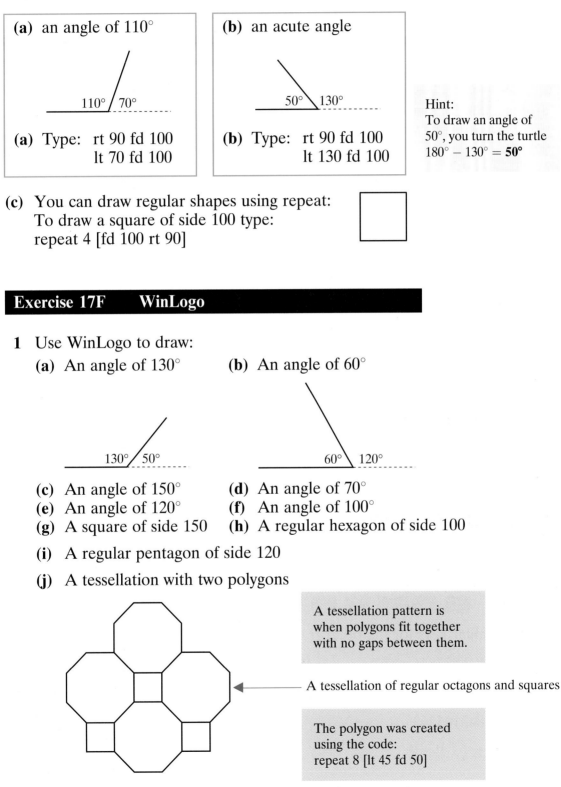

(a) an angle of 110°

110° / 70°

(a) Type: rt 90 fd 100
         lt 70 fd 100

(b) an acute angle

50° \ 130°

(b) Type: rt 90 fd 100
         lt 130 fd 100

Hint:
To draw an angle of
50°, you turn the turtle
180° − 130° = **50°**

(c) You can draw regular shapes using repeat:
To draw a square of side 100 type:
repeat 4 [fd 100 rt 90]

Exercise 17F   WinLogo

1 Use WinLogo to draw:

(a) An angle of 130°   **(b)** An angle of 60°

130° / 50°   60° \ 120°

(c) An angle of 150°   **(d)** An angle of 70°
(e) An angle of 120°   **(f)** An angle of 100°
(g) A square of side 150   **(h)** A regular hexagon of side 100

(i) A regular pentagon of side 120

(j) A tessellation with two polygons

A tessellation pattern is
when polygons fit together
with no gaps between them.

A tessellation of regular octagons and squares

The polygon was created
using the code:
repeat 8 [lt 45 fd 50]

17.7 Fractions

Example 5

(a) Find $\frac{2}{3}$ of £39.81

(b) Reduce $\frac{90}{135}$ to its lowest terms.

(c) Place the following fractions in order of size, starting with the smallest.

$$\frac{11}{13}, \ \frac{7}{9}, \ \frac{21}{26}, \ \frac{6}{7}, \ \frac{16}{19}$$

(d) Change the mixed number $16\frac{12}{17}$ into an improper fraction.

(e) Change $\frac{423}{17}$ to a mixed number.

You can use the fraction key on your calculator to answer the type of questions you met in Chapter 6.

Your fraction key may look like this:

To enter $\frac{2}{3}$ press:

(a) Press:

2 a^{b/c} 3 × 3 9 · 8 1 =

Answer: £26.54

Press the multiplication key for 'of' in $\frac{2}{3}$ of £39.81

(b) Press:

9 0 a^{b/c} 1 3 5 =

Answer: $\frac{2}{3}$

(c) You can use the decimal equivalent of each fraction to help order them.

Press

and similar keys for the other fractions to give:

$\frac{11}{13} = 0.846153846\ldots$ $\frac{7}{9} = 0.777777777\ldots$

$\frac{21}{26} = 0.807692307\ldots$ $\frac{6}{7} = 0.857142857\ldots$

$\frac{16}{19} = 0.842105263\ldots$

Answer: $\frac{7}{9}, \ \frac{21}{26}, \ \frac{16}{19}, \ \frac{11}{13}, \ \frac{6}{7}$

The decimal equivalent is found by dividing the numerator of the fraction by the denominator.

(d) Press:

Answer $= \frac{284}{17}$

1 is $\frac{17}{17}$,

2 is $\frac{34}{17}$ $2 \times 17 = 34$

3 is $\frac{51}{17}$ $3 \times 17 = 51$

. . . . . .

16 is $\frac{272}{17}$ $16 \times 17 = 272$

$16\frac{12}{17}$ is $\frac{284}{17}$ $272 + 12 = 284$

(e) Press:

[4] [2] [3] [$a^{b/c}$] [1] [7] [=]

Answer $= 24\frac{15}{17}$

Exercise 17G   Scientific calculator

1 Calculate:

(a) $\frac{3}{5}$ of £63.45   (b) $\frac{7}{9}$ of £167.76   (c) $\frac{11}{12}$ of $625.32

2 Reduce these fractions to their lowest terms.

(a) $\frac{140}{252}$ (b) $\frac{176}{192}$ (c) $\frac{264}{282}$ (d) $\frac{57}{76}$ (e) $\frac{315}{560}$

3 Place these fractions in order of size starting with the smallest.

$\frac{27}{28}, \frac{35}{36}, \frac{16}{17}, \frac{12}{13}, \frac{55}{59}$

4 Change these mixed numbers to improper fractions.

(a) $13\frac{5}{9}$ (b) $23\frac{14}{17}$ (c) $9\frac{17}{19}$ (d) $45\frac{56}{57}$

5 Change these improper fractions to mixed numbers.

(a) $\frac{165}{132}$ (b) $\frac{203}{19}$ (c) $\frac{433}{212}$ (d) $\frac{1965}{18}$

Exercise 17H   Scientific calculator

1 Match the total

Use **all** of the numbers in each question to make a total of 24. You can use brackets, $+$, $-$, $\times$ and $\div$. The first three are done for you.

(a) 6, 6, 2 and 2 $6 \times 2 + 6 \times 2 = 24$

(b) 1, 2, 6 and 7 $(7 + 6 - 1) \times 2 = 24$

(c) 1, 5, 6 and 6 $6 \times 5 \div 1 - 6 = 24$

Remember to do all the calculations in the right order. There is more on this on page 205.

(d) 2, 5, 6 and 7   **(e)** 3, 3, 9 and 6

(f) 2, 5, 9 and 8   **(g)** 4, 5, 9 and 8

(h) 4, 4, 8 and 9   **(i)** 3, 4, 8 and 9

(j) 1, 4, 4 and 7   **(k)** 1, 2, 2 and 6

(l) 1, 7, 9 and 8   **(m)** 1, 3, 8 and 9

(n) 3, 3, 7 and 7   **(p)** 2, 3, 6 and 7

2   Cycles

What happens to the place value of the digits 1, 4, 2, 8, 5 and 7 when you multiply the number 142857 by the numbers 1 to 6?

3   Fibonacci sequence

This sequence is called the Fibonacci sequence
1, 1, 2, 3, 5, 8, 13, 21, 34, 55, 89, ...

(a) Find the next 5 terms.

(b) Choose **any** 10 consecutive terms from the Fibonacci sequence. Add them together and divide this total by the 7th term of your chosen 10. Write down your answer.

(c) Repeat part **(b)** for a different ten consecutive terms.

(d) Repeat part **(b)** for a third time.

(e) Write down what you discovered.

In the Fibonacci sequence, any term after the second is found by adding the previous two terms:

1, 1, 2, 3, 5, 8, 13,

$2 = 1 + 1$

$13 = 8 + 5$

Index

Acute angle 30, 31
Addition
  2-digit numbers mentally 19–21
  decimals 114–116
  fractions 96–98
  mentally 8–11, 19–21
  multiples of 10: 11–12
  multiples of 10 to 2–digit number
    18–19
  multiples of 100: 14
  on paper 22
Algebra 63–72
  collecting letters 65–66
  collecting like terms 66–68
  expression 66–69
  letters representing numbers
    63–4
  like terms 66–68
  multiplication 69–70
  multiplying terms together 70–72
  simplifying expressions 68–69
  solving equations 212–214
  substitution 207–208
  terms 66–68
am [time] 144
Angles 30–40
  acute 30, 31
  at a point 35–37
  circle 35
  drawing 32, 262–264
  estimating 33–34
  measurement 31–32
  obtuse 30, 31
  protractor 31–32
  right 30, 31, 33, 34
  shapes 37–38
  straight line 34
  straight lines crossing 35
  triangle 39–40
Approximation symbol 54
Arc 135–136
Area 215–226, 230–231
  composite shape 222–223
  curved shapes 224–226
  rectangle 218–220
  right-angled triangle 220–222
Averages 232–246
  data comparison 244–245
  mean 241–242, 260
  median 238–240, 260

  mode 232–237, 260
  range 242–244, 260
  spreadsheet calculations 259–262

Bar chart 185, 187, 189, 235–237
Bar line graph 186, 187, 189
Bi-modal 233
BIDMAS 205, 208

Calculators 254–266
Capacity 142–143
Casio calculator 254
Celsius scale 147–148
Centimetre 141, 143–144
Chance see probability
Checking by estimating 16–18
Circle 135–136
  angles 35
  arc 135–136
  circumference 135–136
  diameter 135–136
  radius 135–136
Circumference 135–136
Class interval 195, 197
Clock times
  12-hour clock 144–145
  24-hour clock 144–145
Computers 254–266
Cone 137–140
Continuous data 193–195
Conversion graphs 177–181
Coordinates
  all quadrants 174–175
  drawing grids 176
  first quadrant 168–171
  plotting 170–171
Counting on or back 19, 156–158
Cube 137–140, 227–228
Cuboid 137–140, 229–230
Cuisenaire rods 203
Cylinder 137–140

Data
  bar chart 185, 187, 189
  bar line graph 186, 187, 189
  class interval 195, 197
  collection 182–184
  comparison 244–245
  continuous 193–195
  discrete 193–195

  display 185–188
  dual bar graph 191–193
  frequency table 182–184
  grouping 195–199
  line graph 193
  organization 182–184
  pictogram 185, 186
  spreadsheet calculations 259–262
  survey 183
  tally chart 182–183
  types 193–195
Data handling 182–200, 259–262
Decimal point 112
Decimals 112–124
  addition 114–116
  dividing by 10, 100, 1000: 118–119
  dividing by whole numbers 122–
    123
  fractions 126–129
  multiplying by 10, 100, 1000: 117–
    118
  multiplying by whole
    numbers 120–121
  ordering decimal numbers 123–
    124
  percentages 126–129
  subtraction 114–116
Degrees
  angles 29
  Celsius 147–148
  Fahrenheit 177
  temperature 147–148, 177
  triangle 39–40
Denominator 86, 96, 97
Diagonals 134
Diameter 135–136
Digit value 1, 5
Discrete data 193–195
Division 41–62
  3-digit number by 1-digit number
    57–58, 60–61
  3-digit number by 2-digit number
    58–61
  decimals by 10, 100, 1000: 118–119
  decimals by whole numbers
    122–123
  factors 49–51
  remainders 44–45
  up to 10 × 10: 45–47
Dot patterns 73–75

Drawing
   angles 32, 262–264
   shapes 262–264
   solid shapes 138–139
   Dual bar graph 191–193

Equal parts 86
Equations
   line on graph 171–172
   number machines 210–212
   solving 209–214
   straight line on graph 171–172
Equivalent fractions 93–96
Estimating angles 33–34
Estimating as a check 16–18
Even numbers 47
Events probability 105–106

Factor star 52
Factors 49–51, 94
Fahrenheit scale 177
Fibonacci sequence 255
Foot 143–144
Formulae 201–208, 214
   algebraic 207–208
   BIDMAS 205, 208
   letters for unknowns 203–205
   not same as equations 209–210
   two operations 205–207
   using letters for numbers 202–203
   using words 201–202
Fractions 86–99
   addition 96–98
   calculator 264–266
   cancelling 94
   denominator 86, 96, 97
   equivalent 93–96
   improper fractions 88–90
   mixed numbers 88–90
   numerator 86, 97
   of quantity 91–93
   percentages 126–129
   simplest form 94
   subtraction 96–98
Frequency table 182–184, 234–235

Graphs 168–181
   conversion graphs 177–181
   coordinates in all quadrants
     174–175
   coordinates in first quadrant
     168–169
   equation of straight line 171–172
   grid 168, 176
   line graph 193
   lines on 171–174

origin 170, 176
   scale not starting at zero 189
   x-axis 170, 176
   y-axis 170, 176
Grid 168, 176
Grouped data 195–199

Hemisphere 137–140
Horizontal number line 160–165

Imperial measures 143–144,
   179–181
Improper fractions 88–90
Inch 180
Indices 205
Information 182
Inverse number machines 210–212
Inverse operations 81–83, 210

Kilogram 181
Kilometre 143–144, 179
Kite 133–134, 169

Letters representing numbers
   63–64
Letters representing shapes 132
Like terms 66–68
Likelihood of event 100–102
Likelihood scale 102–103
Line graph 193
Litre 142, 143–144, 180

Matchstick patterns 73–75
Mathematical investigation 247–253
Mean 241–242, 260
Measurement 141–146
   angles 31–32
   capacity 142
   conversion graphs 177–181
   imperial measures 143–144,
     179–181
   length 141
   temperature 147–148
   time 144–145
   turns 29
Median 238–240, 260
Mental maths
   addition 8–11, 19–21
   subtraction 8–11, 19–21
Metre 141
Microsoft Excel 254, 260
Middle value 238
Mile 143–144, 179
Millilitre 142
Millimetre 141, 180
Modal number 232, 237

Mode 232–237, 260
Multiples 47–49
Multiplication 41–62
   2- and 3-digit numbers by 1-digit
     number 52–55
   3-digit number by 2-digit number
     56, 60–61
   algebra 69–70
   algebraic terms together 70–72
   decimals by 10, 100, 1000: 117–118
   decimals by whole numbers
     120–121
   up to 10×10 45–47
   Multiplication tables 11, 41–42,
     43, 47–49

'name the lines' 172
Negative numbers 147–167
Net 140
Number
   counting on or back 156–158
   key points 24–25
   large 188–191
   larger than 1000: 3–4
   mixed 88–90
   negative 147–167
   ordering 5–8
   positive 147–167
   representing probability 103–104
   sequences 83–85
   series 83–85
   square 51–52
Number line
   horizontal 160–165
   positive and negative
     numbers 158–160
   vertical 153–158
Number machine
   inverse 210–212
   number pattern 76–80, 83
   solving equations 210–212
   spreadsheet 258–259
Number patterns 73–85
   continuing 163–167
   horizontal number lines 163–167
   number machine 76–80, 83
Numerator 86, 97

Obtuse angle 30, 31
Odd numbers 47
Ordering
   decimal numbers 123–124
   positive and negative numbers
     163–165
   temperatures 149–151
   whole numbers 5–8

Origin 170, 176
Outcome, probability 105–110

Parallel lines 132
Parallelogram 133–134
Percentages 125–130
    calculators 257–258
    decimals 126–129
    fractions 126–129
    of amount 129–130
Perimeter 215–220, 230–231
Perpendicular lines 132
Pictogram 185, 186
Pint 143–144, 180
Place value 1–3, 5
Place value diagram 2, 3–4
pm [time] 144
Positive numbers 147–167
Pound 181
Powers of numbers 205
Prism 137–140
Probability 100–111
    calculating 107–110
    certainty 100–102
    events 105–106
    impossibility 100–102
    language of 100–102
    likelihood 100–102
    likelihood scale 102–103
    likely 101–102
    numbers representing 103–104
    outcomes 105–106
    possibility 100–102
    unlikely 101–102
    value from 0 to 1 103–104
Problem solving 247–253
Protractor 31–32
Pyramid 137–140

Quadrilaterals 133–134

Radius 135–136
Range 242–244, 260
Rectangle 133–134

area 218–220
    perimeter 217–220
Reflective symmetry 26–28
Remainders 44–45
Reversing operations 81–83, 210–212
Rhombus 133–134
Right angle 30, 31, 33, 34
Rod train 203
Rotation 29
Rounding 12–14, 15–16

Sequences 83–85, 255–256
Series 83–85
Shaking hands problem 247–253
Shapes 132–140, 146
    angles 37–38
    composite 222–223
    construction 136
    curved 224–226
    drawing 138–139
    net 140
    quadrilaterals 133–134
    rotational symmetry 26–27
    solid 137–140
    symmetrical 26–28
    volume 227–228
Simplifying problems 248
Solving equations 209–214
Sphere 137–140
Spreadsheet 255–256
    data handling 259–262
    number machines 258–259
Square 133–134
Square numbers 51–52
Square root 52, 254
Straight lines
    angle 34
    angle where they cross 35
    on graphs 171–174
    parallel 132
    perpendicular 132
Strategy for problems 249
Subtraction
    2-digit numbers mentally 19–21

decimals 114–116
    fractions 96–98
    mentally 8–11, 19–21
    multiple of 10 from 2-digit number
        18–19
    multiples of 10: 11–12
    multiples of 100: 14
    on paper 23–24
Survey 183
Symbols
    ≈ [approximate] 54, 224
    ° [angles] 29
    °C [angles] 147, 177
    °F [angles] 177
    % [percentage] 125
Symmetry 26–29
    reflective 26–28
    rotational 26–27
    shapes 26–28

Tally chart 182–183
Temperature 147–148, 177–178
    ordering by size 149–151
    positive and negative 149–153
    thermometer 147–148, 149–153, 160
Term 66–68
Tessellation 263
Testing predictions 252–253
Thermometer 147–148, 149–153, 160
Trapezium 133–134, 169
Triangle
    angles 39–40
    drawing 262–264
    right–angled 220–222
Turtle 262

Vertical number line 153–158
Volume 227–231

Winlogo program 254, 262–264

x-axis 170, 176

y-axis 170, 176